K–3 Overhead Manipulatives

in Action

—

Barbara Bando Irvin

Table of Contents

Overhead and Classroom Manipulatives

All of the overhead manipulatives used in the activities in this book and suggested classroom manipulatives are available from Learning Resources. The overhead manipulatives are listed in italic.

Required Materials

Three Bear Family™
LER 733 *Three Bear Family™ Overhead Attribute Tiles*
LER 725 Three Bear Family™ Counters

Attribute Blocks
LER 1386 *Overhead Attribute Blocks*
LER 1277 Attribute Blocks Desk Set or
LER 1278 Attribute Blocks Pocket Set

Pattern Blocks
LER 640 *Overhead Pattern Blocks*
LER 134 Plastic Pattern Blocks or
LER 334 Wooden Pattern Blocks

Numbers 1–100 and Counters
LER 378 *Overhead Numbers 1–100*
LER 381 Number Squares 1–100
LER 131 *Transparent Counters*

Base Ten Blocks
LER 650 *Overhead Base Ten Blocks*
LER 930 Plastic Base Ten Starter Set or
LER 231 Wooden Base Ten Starter Set

Clocks
LER 570 *Overhead Clock Dials*

Coins
LER 625 *Overhead Coin Set*
LER 101 Coin Set or
LER 95–99 Money in Bulk

Fraction Circles
LER 315 *Overhead Fraction Circles*
LER 115 Circular Fraction Set

Color Squares
LER 478 *Overhead Color Squares*

Spinners
LER 158 *Transparent Spinners*

Shape Tracer Sets
LER 279 *Shape Tracer Set*
LER 280 *Shape Tracer Extension Set*

Additional Resources

LER 730 Three Bear Family™ Fun
LER 734 Three Bear Family™ Activity Book
LER 735 Three Bear Family™ Attribute Cards

LER 1381 Giant Attribute Blocks
LER 1385 Attribute Block Template
LER 1200 Attribute Block Activity Cards

LER 1391 Pattern Block Template
LER 267 Pattern Block Rubber Stamps
LER 335 Pattern Block Activity Pack
LER 264 Pattern Block Activity Cards
LER 330 Pattern Block Party
LER 336 Patternables Activity Book

LER 1330 Hundred Number Board
LER 374 *Large Transparent Counters*
LER 194 Stackable Counting Chips
LER 193 Color Counting Chips

LER 128 Base Ten Block Stamps
LER 230 Base Ten Activity Book

LER 112 Pupil Clocks

LER 102 Coin Stamps—Heads
LER 103 Coin Stamps—Tails
LER 107 Coin Matching Cards
LER 108 Making Change Cards
LER 80 Magnetic Money
LER 85 Currency-X-Change
LER 81 Fun With Money Activity Book
LER 105 Money Activity Book
LER 202 Activity Coin Cube

LER 250 Fraction Activity Flash Cards
LER 1397 Circle Template

LER 203 Square Color Tiles

LER 147 Color Probability Spinners
LER 148 Number Probability Spinners
LER 159 Probability Kit

Introduction

Overhead Manipulatives in Action, K–3 is a collection of 48 lessons designed to help teachers make the best use of eight different manipulatives on the overhead projector. The lessons have been carefully developed to present explorations and demonstrations with concrete models. Engaging children in explorations—learning by doing, thinking, and talking—not only improves mathematics skills, but also visual perception, memory, and critical thinking skills. Problem-solving strategies, communication, and socialization skills are also greatly enhanced.

This teacher resource book is organized into eight sections, focusing on the following overhead manipulatives:

- Three Bear Family™ Attribute Tiles
- Attribute Blocks
- Pattern Blocks
- Numbers 1–100
- Base Ten Blocks
- Clock Dials
- Coins
- Fraction Circles

Some lessons also feature activities with Transparent Counters, Color Squares, Transparent Spinners, Shape Tracer, and Shape Tracer Extension Sets.

The lessons in *Overhead Manipulatives in Action, K–3* cover a wide range of mathematical topics and practical skills that can be integrated into any existing mathematics curriculum, kindergarten through third grade. They include:

- sorting
- classifying
- counting
- comparing
- patterns
- sequences
- place value
- numeration
- addition
- subtraction
- shape identification
- congruence
- similarity
- symmetry
- coin identification
- coin values
- counting money
- making change
- telling time
- figuring elapsed time
- fraction concepts
- comparing fractions
- estimation
- mental computation

The activities build sequentially on children's prior learning to ensure a logical progression of skill development and to make the connection between different mathematical topics. Refer to the Table of Contents to find a specific topic and integrate it into your mathematics curriculum.

NCTM Standards

Using NCTM's *Curriculum and Evaluation Standards for School Mathematics* (1989) as a guideline for developing the lessons in this book, children will be actively involved in activities that develop mathematics understanding and relationships. By incorporating the first four process-oriented standards for any mathematical topic, they will also be better able to solve problems, apply reasoning abilities, make connections, and communicate ideas.

The activities provided afford various opportunities for using problem-solving strategies such as making lists, drawing pictures, using the process of elimination, and writing an equation for a problem. Emphasis is placed on reasoning and critical thinking skills when children are asked what they think about a problem, how many possible ways they can find to solve a problem, or whether they can justify their decisions or answers. By discussing, showing and telling, making books, and writing short descriptions to share ideas with classmates, children acquire the language as well as the concepts of mathematics. Since it is important that children connect ideas both among and within areas of mathematics, some of the topics in this program use more than one type of overhead manipulative.

Using *Overhead Manipulatives in Action, K–3*

Overhead Manipulatives in Action consists of eight sections of six lessons each. In addition to the 48 lessons, teaching suggestions are included at the beginning and several forms (Student Progress Chart, Family Letter, and Certificates) are included at the back of this book to facilitate classroom management and communication.

Each section begins with a overview of the content and materials needed, and a *Getting Started* activity, followed by one or three pages replicating the overhead manipulatives. Except for the reduced size of Numbers 1–100, all of the manipulatives are shown in actual size.

 ## The Lesson Plan

Each lesson consists of a page of teaching notes and an overhead blackline master. The teaching notes contain the following information and types of activities:

Objective	The goal of the lesson.
Vocabulary	A list of mathematical terms to focus on the language of mathematics.
Materials	A list of materials to help you prepare for your presentation and for student activities.
Warm-Up	Tasks to review necessary prerequisite skills or to set the stage for the prime activity of the lesson.
Activity	Step-by-step directions to ensure well-planned demonstrations and explorations for a specific math objective. Set-up procedures, suggested questions, and even some sample scripts are included.
Practice	Suggestions to enable children to work individually, in pairs, or in small cooperative groups to complete an activity.
Wrap-Up	Summarizes the lesson and checks children's understanding.

Some lessons contain a *Challenge* or *Extension Activity* for additional practice. Although many suggestions are provided to help you implement the lessons, only you can decide how to organize the children and materials to suit your classroom needs.

You can use the overhead blackline masters to make an overhead transparency or a student worksheet. It is essential that you duplicate copies of the overhead blackline transparencies for children when you are working with the transparency on the projector so that they can actively participate. Several of the overhead blackline masters are generic enough to be used with other overhead manipulative lessons or with other curriculum topics. For example, the Three Bear Family™ scene on page 8, the clowns on page 54, and the place value mat on page 63 can be used over and over with many lessons. Likewise, some pages may be used with another manipulative. For example, try playing the *Trade Up Game* on page 70 with coins instead of base ten blocks.

Using the Overhead Projector

Using manipulatives on the overhead projector will help you become a more effective educator. Your demonstrations will become more colorful and filled with movement. Also, by facing the children, you can maintain eye contact with them as well as see whether they are on task. Several student response techniques may be employed besides calling out answers or raising hands; children can hold up cards for you to see and no one else, indicate thumbs-up, thumbs-down responses, or use "air writing." Whichever response technique you use, be sure to inform children about it before the lesson begins.

Each lesson lists the materials needed to carry out the activity. However, here is a list of materials you should have available for every lesson:
   ◆ Set of erasable overhead color pens
   ◆ Blank transparencies
   ◆ Sheets of blank paper or lightweight tagboard
   ◆ Spray bottle of water
   ◆ Paper towel or cloth
   ◆ Extra overhead projector bulb

Placing a blank transparency over the overhead master transparency will allow you to move or remove all the manipulative pieces at one time or to draw lines or write answers without messing up the original. Use sheets of paper to play "cover-up" games, "flash" games, or to expose only portions of a transparency at a time.

To facilitate lesson presentations, arrange the overhead manipulatives on a piece of acetate or tagboard and place it near the projector. For example, having all 48 Three Bear Family™ Attribute Tiles sorted and in sight will help you find the tiles quickly as you model a mathematical situation.

Student Materials

Besides having the appropriate classroom manipulatives available, the following materials should also be handy, to enable the students to complete the activities:
   ◆ Sheets of blank paper
   ◆ Spiral theme book or tablet
   ◆ Set of crayons or color markers
   ◆ Pencils with erasers
   ◆ Scissors
   ◆ Paste, glue, or tape
   ◆ Pocket envelopes or plastic ziplock bags

You may also wish children to have basic four-function calculators to help them find multiple solutions to some problems or to verify their estimates or solutions.

Encourage children to make their own sets of manipulatives and store them in envelopes or plastic bags. This will get them into the habit of using the materials to understand problems and to figure out solutions. Also, make some of the manipulatives available at all times so children can use their leisure time to create patterns or invent new problems.

Class Management

Depending on the availability of classroom manipulatives and children's ability, children can work individually, in pairs, in small cooperative groups, or as an entire class. Some activities are more conducive than others for working together.

To keep track of a child's progress, Student Progress Charts are provided. A generic Family Letter allows you to suggest how family members can help students learn more about a mathematical concept or skill. For children needing more tangible means of encouragement or recognition, three types of certificates are provided.

Overhead Manipulatives in Action, K–3
© 1992 Learning Resources, Inc.

Three Bear Family™ Attribute Tiles

Introduction

The set of *Three Bear Family™ Overhead Attribute Tiles* offers an appealing and meaningful way to present basic mathematical concepts and problem-solving strategies. The attributes of color and size enable children to observe similarities and differences among the bears, use their reasoning abilities to sort and classify, and work with patterns. The bears can also be used to lend a realistic approach to the study of quantitative concepts. Children can learn to count objects and compare numbers as well as to understand the basic operations by telling stories about the bears. Working with the Three Bear Family can be a natural, concrete prelude to the many mathematical concepts children will encounter when working with attribute blocks, color cubes and counters.

The Three Bear Family™ Activities

Pages   7– 8   Sort and Classify
        9–10   Patterns
        11–12   Count and Compare
        13–14   Acting out Addition
        15–16   Acting out Subtraction
        17–18   Making Arrangements

 ## Getting Organized

Materials you will need:
- ◆ *Three Bear Family™ Overhead Attribute Tiles* (LER 733)
- ◆ One transparency each of pages 8, 10, 12, 14, 16, 18
- ◆ Blank transparencies, overhead pens, sheet of paper

Materials students will need:
- ◆ *Three Bear Family™ Counters* (LER 725)
- ◆ Copies of pages 6, 8, 10, 12, 14, 16, 18
- ◆ Crayons or color markers, scissors, paste, sheets of paper

Children can use the cutouts of the *Three Bear Family™ Overhead Attribute Tiles* on page 6 if *Three Bear Family™ Counters* are not available. They can also use the cutouts for cut-and-paste activities with pages 8, 10, 12, 14, 16, and 18. Have children color three each of the Papa and Mama Bears and six each of the Baby Bears in the four colors red, green, yellow, and blue, and then cut them out. Or duplicate page 6 on red, green, yellow, and blue paper for children to cut apart.

 ## Getting Started

Introduce the *Three Bear Family* to the class by giving each pair a collection of 12 bears, one of each size and color. Permit them to handle and talk about the bears. Observe what they do with the bears. Also listen to the vocabulary children use to describe the bears or their actions. Ask children about the bears and what they are doing with them. Use this free exploration to help you pace the activities presented on pages 7–18. If children do not know the four colors of the bears or cannot distinguish between the sizes, use this *Getting Started* session to introduce them formally to the colors red, blue, yellow and green and the sizes large, medium and small before continuing on to the activities in this section.

Three Bear Family™ Tiles

Sort and Classify

✓ Objective

To sort the bears by color and size.

Vocabulary

alike, different, color, red, green, blue, yellow, size, large, medium, small, sort

Materials

Three Bear Family™ Overhead Attribute Tiles, transparency of page 8; *Three Bear Family™ Counters*, student copies of page 8, colored cutouts of page 6, paste

Warm-Up

Alike and Different. Play the Alike and Different Flash Game. Tell children that you are going to show a pair of bears on the projector for only a few seconds. Direct children to clap their hands if the bears are *alike* and to snap their fingers if the bears are *different*. Do seven or eight pairs of bears in quick succession.

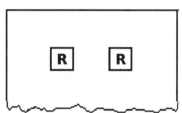

Activity 1

Three Bear Family's House. (Sort by color) Distribute page 8 and at least 12 bears, one of each color and size. Place the transparency of page 8 on the projector. First, ask children to identify the house, yard, pool, and tree. Then place bear tiles in the appropriate locations as you tell a story like this:

> **There are several bears here today.**
> **The red bears went into the house.**
> **The blue bears went into the pool.**
> **The green bears climbed the tree and**
> **the yellow bears went into the yard.**

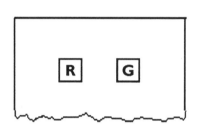

Pause after each sentence so that children can follow along and imitate your actions. Observe children as they place the bears in the appropriate locations for each color. Let them know that size is not important when sorting by color.

Practice

Ask children to tell their own stories about sorting the bears by color into the four locations shown on the page. As an assignment, have them paste colored cutouts (page 6) of the bears onto page 8 to show their sorting procedures. Display the completed pages in the classroom.

Activity 2

Sort by Size. Follow the same procedure used for sorting by color. This time designate only three locations into which children can place their bears. After the sorting, recap: Papa Bears are large, Mama Bears are medium, Baby Bears are small. Remind students that color is not important when sorting by size.

Wrap-Up

Discuss the sorting procedures children used. Have them "show and tell" their vignettes.

The Three Bear Family's House

Patterns

✓ Objective

To identify, copy, extend, and create patterns.

Vocabulary

pattern, copy, extend, predict

Materials

Three Bear Family™ Overhead Attribute Tiles, sheet of paper, transparency of page 10; *Three Bear Family™ Counters*, student copies of page 10, colored cutouts from page 6, paste, string

Warm-Up

Copy Patterns. Each pair or small group of children will need a set of bear counters and a copy of page 10. Display a simple *ab* bear pattern consisting of red and blue Papa Bears—RBRBRB—on the transparency on the projector. Tell children that the bears are in line to go to a music concert. Ask them to identify the bears in the line from one end to the other (left to right). Then have them copy the pattern. Go around the room to check the results. Repeat this activity using more colors and sizes, gradually increasing the number of attributes of bears used. After completing this activity a few times, ask children what a pattern is.

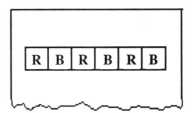

Activity

Summer Show. (Extending patterns) Arrange an *abc* parade of bears such as **Yellow Baby Bear, Blue Baby Bear, Red Baby Bear, Yellow Baby Bear, Blue Baby Bear, Red Baby Bear** on the projector. Cover the line of bears with a sheet of paper. Tell children to pay close attention to the bears as you uncover each bear one by one. Turn on the projector. Show the first bear and ask the class to make a choral response to indicate which color is being uncovered each time. Have children follow along with their set of bear counters as you uncover each bear. When you get to the last bear, keep the paper in place and ask individuals if they can predict the color of the next bear, the next bear, and so on. Add a **Yellow Baby Bear, Blue Baby Bear,** and **Red Baby Bear** to the line of bears. Repeat the activity.

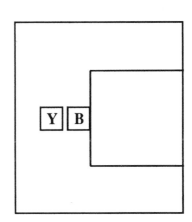

Practice

Show a simple pattern on the projector and direct children to make the parade longer using the same pattern and their bear counters. Some children may wish to create a bear pattern and extend it for a long distance, such as around the bulletin board, using the cutouts on page 6 and stringing them together.

Wrap-Up

Discuss the results. Have children check each other's work. If a cut-and-paste activity was assigned for page 10, display the patterns in the classroom and discuss them.

Summer Show

Overhead Manipulatives in Action, K–3
© 1992 Learning Resources, Inc.

Count and Compare

 Objectives

To count a given number of objects.
To compare sets of numbers.

Vocabulary

count, numbers 1-10, compare, equals, more than, less than, fewer

Materials

Three Bear Family™ Overhead Attribute Tiles, overhead pen, blank transparency, transparency of page 12; *Three Bear Family™ Counters*, student copies of page 12, pencils

Activity 1

On the Road. (Counting bears) Display five bears on the projector. Ask children how many bears there are. Then have several children take turns counting the bears to verify the amount. Have children count out five bears at their desks. Write the numeral 5 on the projector next to the bears after they have been counted. Repeat this activity for several other numbers.

Reverse the activity. Write a numeral from 5–10, say, 7, on a blank transparency. Ask children to write a 7 on top of a blank sheet of paper and then count out 7 bears. After children have counted out their bears, ask a volunteer to count out 7 bears on the projector.

Activity 2

Comparing Numbers. Distribute page 12 and at least 15 bears to each child or pair. Display a transparency of page 12 on the projector. Tell a story about the bears:

> Two groups of bears are taking a ride.
> Six bears are riding the bus. Four bears are in the truck.
> Which group has more (fewer) bears?

After children decide that more bears are riding the bus, ask them how they know. Demonstrate the one-to-one correspondence matching procedure to show the comparison. Direct children to use this procedure or to use counting when comparing sets of objects. Repeat this activity with equivalent and nonequivalent sets of objects. Introduce the symbols <, =, and > after several groups of bears have been compared and children are ready to comprehend the new symbols.

Practice

Ask children to make up stories about the bears riding the bus and the truck. Tell them to be prepared to share their stories with the class and that they can use matching (one-to-one correspondence) to compare the groups of bears.

Wrap-Up

Have children share their stories with the class and tell how they determined which group had more bears.

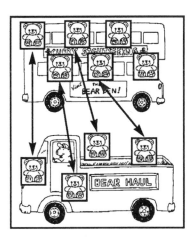

On the Road

Three Bear Family™ Attribute Tiles

Overhead Manipulatives in Action, K–3
© 1992 Learning Resources, Inc.

Acting out Addition

✓ Objective

To understand the operation of addition by using counters to model the process.

Vocabulary

add, sum, total, in all, altogether

Materials

Three Bear Family™ Overhead Attribute Tiles, transparency of page 14, overhead pen, blank transparency; *Three Bear Family™ Counters*, student copies of page 14, colored cutouts of the bears (page 6), paste

Warm-Up

Ask three children to come to the front of the room. Then ask two more children to join the other three. Ask the class how many children are standing in front of the room. Have them verify their answer by counting the children.

Activity

Home Sweet Home. (Acting out addition) Distribute a copy of page 14 and ten bears to each child or pair. Display a transparency of page 14 on the projector. Tell an addition basic facts story similar to this one:

> **There are some bears in the house.**
> **Three bears are listening to music upstairs.**
> **Five bears are talking downstairs.**
> **How many bears are in the house in all (altogether)?** [8]

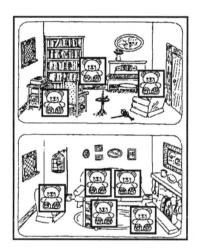

$$3 + 5 = 8$$

Direct children to use their bear counters to act out the story. Recap the story by asking how many bears are upstairs and downstairs, and then how they would find the total number (sum) of bears. [count] Once children understand the concept of addition as the process of *joining together*, gradually introduce a number sentence (equation) to represent each scenario. For the story above, the number sentences $3 + 5 = 8$ or $5 + 3 = 8$ describe the problem.

Practice

Children can tell their own stories to each other and to you, or they can make Addition Storybooks for the basic facts of addition using colored cutouts of the bears from page 6 and several copies of page 14. Have them write the appropriate number sentence on each page. For variety, children may wish to use copies of pages 8 and 12 in their storybooks.

Wrap-Up

Call on children to act out their addition stories for the class.

Home Sweet Home

Three Bear Family™ Attribute Tiles

Overhead Manipulatives in Action, K–3
© 1992 Learning Resources, Inc.

Acting out Subtraction

✓ Objective

To understand subtraction by using counters to model the process.

Vocabulary

subtract, difference, are left, how many more (fewer)?

Materials

Three Bear Family™ Overhead Attribute Tiles, transparency of page 16, overhead pen, blank transparency; *Three Bear Family™ Counters*, student copies of page 16

Warm-Up

Ask five children to come to the front of the classroom and then direct three of them to go to the back of the classroom. Ask how many children are still standing in front of the classroom. Or ask five children to go to the chalkboard and two other children to stand near the door. Ask how many more children are at the chalkboard.

Activity

Planes and Trains. (Subtraction) Distribute page 16 and ten bears. Display a transparency of page 16 on the projector. Tell a subtraction basic facts story similar to this one:

There are five bears riding the train.
Three bears got off the train.
How many bears are left on the train?

Direct children to use their bear counters to act out the story. Recap the story by asking them how many bears were riding the train, how many bears got off, and then how many bears were still on the train. After a few stories, children will be able to understand subtraction as the process of *taking away*. Then introduce and write appropriate subtraction number sentences for the stories.

Besides using the "take away" concept of subtraction, introduce children to another meaning of subtraction—*comparison*—with a story like this one:

There are three bears in the airplane.
There are five bears on the train.
How many more bears are on the train?

Display the story on the projector using page 18 and eight bear tiles. Have children follow along using a copy of page 16 and their bear counters. Have children create their own comparison subtraction stories and write subtraction number sentences.

Practice

Have children work in cooperative groups and tell subtraction stories.

Wrap-Up

Call on children to act out their subtraction stories for the class.

Three Bear Family™ Attribute Tiles

Planes and Trains

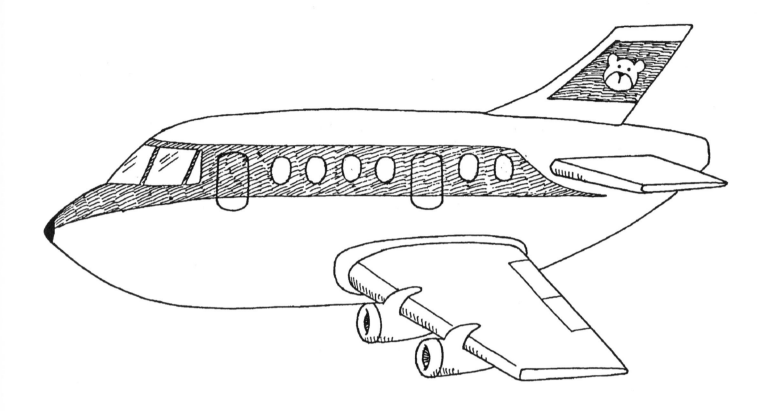

Three Bear Family™ Attribute Tiles

Overhead Manipulatives in Action, K–3
© 1992 Learning Resources, Inc.

Making Arrangements

 Objective

To find as many arrangements as possible for a given number of objects.

Vocabulary
arrangements

Materials
Three Bear Family™ Overhead Attribute Tiles, transparency of page 18; *Three Bear Family™ Counters*, student copies of page 18, pencils, colored cutouts of the bears (page 6), paste, paper

Warm-Up
Place three chairs in front of the classroom facing the class. Ask three volunteers to sit in the chairs. Now ask them to change places. You may wish to have the child keep track of the different arrangements by recording them on the chalkboard. Have children change their seating arrangements until they think that they have found all the different ways.

Activity
In the Park. (Arrangements) Distribute bear counters and a copy of page 18. Have children select any two different-looking bears. Ask them to make all the possible *arrangements* for the two bears. Only two arrangements are possible, for example, red, blue or blue, red. Verify their solutions by displaying them on the projector. Then have children select three different-looking bears to make all possible arrangements. Show an organized list of the six arrangements using the overhead bear tiles. Rather than using color as the dominant feature, suggest that some children use bears of one color in three sizes. Have children paste colored cutouts of the bears onto page 18 to show their organized list of arrangements for a given number of bears.

Practice
Ask children to select four different looking bears and to make all the possible arrangements for them. [24 ways] Direct children to record their findings in an organized list by pasting colored tile cutouts on several copies of page 18 or on blank paper.

Wrap-Up
Discuss the arrangements of the bears. Ask about the positions of the bears in any particular arrangement. It is critical that children realize that there may be several solutions to a problem and that organizing information into a list or using pictures is a valid problem-solving technique.

Challenge Activity
As a class project, suggest finding all possible arrangements of five different-looking bears. [120 ways]

In the Park

Overhead Manipulatives in Action, K–3
© 1992 Learning Resources, Inc.

Attribute Blocks

Introduction

The 30-piece set of *Overhead Attribute Blocks* consists of five geometric shapes in two sizes and three colors, made of transparent plastic. It offers an effective, concrete way to stimulate children to sort and classify and to investigate geometric shapes and patterns. The 60-piece set of *Attribute Blocks* has the added attribute of thickness. Shape Tracer Sets are used in the last lesson to introduce the student to other geometric shapes.

Attribute Block Activities

 ## Getting Organized

Materials you will need:
- ◆ *Overhead Attribute Blocks* (LER 1386)
- ◆ One transparency each of pages 22, 24, 26, 28, 30, 32
- ◆ *Shape Tracer Set* (LER 279) and *Shape Tracer Extension Set* (LER 280)
- ◆ Blank transparencies, overhead pens

Materials students will need:
- ◆ *Attribute Blocks* (Desk Set LER 1277 or Pocket Set LER 1278)
- ◆ Copies of pages 20, 22, 24, 26, 28, 30, 32
- ◆ *Shape Tracer Set* (LER 279) and *Shape Tracer Extension Set* (LER 280)
- ◆ Crayons or color markers, scissors, paste, pencils, paper

To make the 30-piece set of attribute blocks shown on page 20, duplicate three copies per child and have the children color one page each with red, yellow, and blue blocks. Or duplicate page 20 on red, yellow, and blue paper and give each child a sheet of each color to cut apart the blocks.

You may wish to split the classroom sets of 60 pieces into two sets consisting of 30 thin blocks and 30 thick blocks. In this way more children can have an opportunity to work with a set of attribute blocks similar to the overhead set. Reference to a 30-piece set of attribute blocks will mean a set of thick blocks or a set of thin blocks. Of course, the full 60-piece set is needed when dealing with the attribute of thickness.

 ## Getting Started

Permit children to explore with their set of *Attribute Blocks* before you ask any questions or give directions. Observe the children's reactions. One child may sort the blocks by color; another child may build a tower. Listen to their discussions while they "play" with the blocks. Compliment them on their discoveries and encourage them to look at all of the blocks. After a basic curiosity about the blocks is satisfied and the play interest has been fulfilled, children will treat the attribute blocks as classroom learning aids and focus on mathematical concepts rather than the blocks themselves.

Attribute Blocks

Overhead Manipulatives in Action, K–3
© 1992 Learning Resources, Inc.

Attribute Shapes

 Objective
To identify and describe basic geometric shapes.

Vocabulary
color, red, blue, yellow, size, large, small, thick, thin, shape, circle, square, rectangle, triangle, hexagon

Materials
Overhead Attribute Blocks, transparency of page 22, overhead pens, blank transparencies, paper; *Attribute Blocks*, student copies of page 22, pencils

Warm-Up
Three Colors. Children should have a set of blocks at their desks or tables. Display the large red circle on the projector. Ask children whether they know its color. Tell them that it is *red*. Ask children to find the same block and hold it up for all to see. Ask what color it is. Ask them to find another red block and then another, until all of the red blocks are found. Ask if they can find something red in the classroom. Repeat the activity for the colors *yellow* and *blue*. Next, discuss the attributes of *size* and *thickness*.

Activity
Five Shapes. Distribute page 22 and display a transparency of that page on the overhead projector as you introduce the five shapes—*circle, square, rectangle, triangle, hexagon*—one at a time. Although many children may be able to identify the shapes, they may never have discussed them in terms of *sides* and *corners*. When talking about each shape, ask if it has sides and corners as well as how many sides and corners. Ask why the square and the rectangle are different even though each has four sides and four corners. To avoid confusion, present the shapes in one size and color, for example, use only the large red blocks. Then look at all the shapes in blue and in yellow.

Practice
I'm Thinking of a Shape. Place a block, such as the large blue triangle, on the projector, and cover it with a sheet of paper. Give each child or pair a 30-piece set of blocks. Have children ask questions about the color, shape, and size of your block that can be answered *yes* or *no*. After asking a series of questions and using the problem-solving strategy, *process of elimination*, children should finally determine that your block is a large blue triangle.

Wrap-Up
Show and Tell. Display the large red hexagon on the projector. Ask children, one by one, to come to the projector or to hold up a block at their desks and tell everyone about its color, shape, and size.

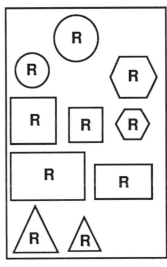

Students will also show <u>thick</u> red shapes.

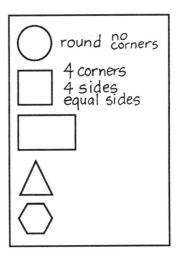

Attribute Blocks

Five Shapes

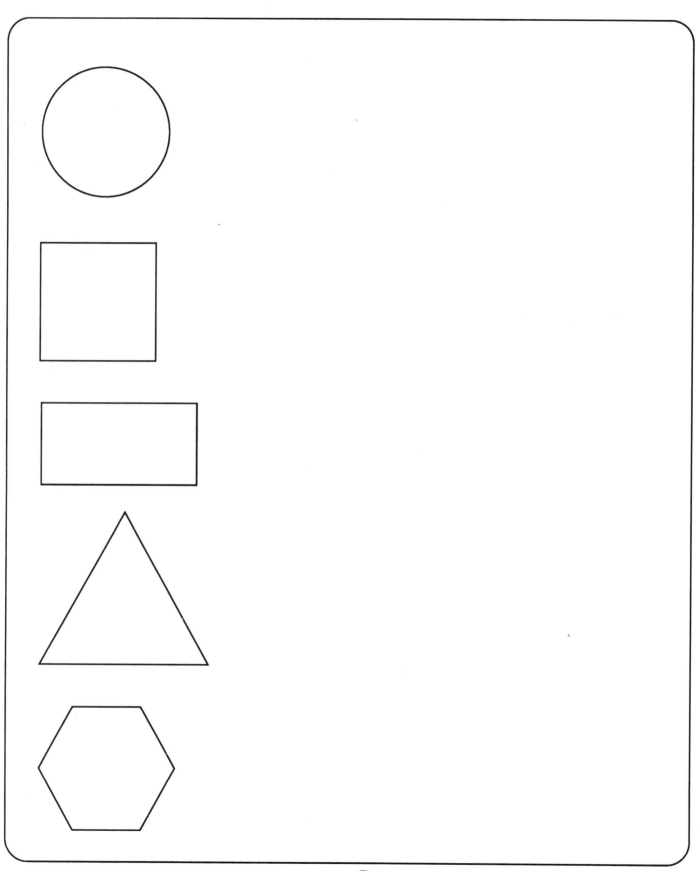

Overhead Manipulatives in Action, K–3
© 1992 Learning Resources, Inc.

Two Groups

 Objectives

To sort objects by color, shape, and size.
To sort and classify objects into two groups.

Vocabulary

sort, color, size, shape, thickness, is, is not

Materials

Overhead Attribute Blocks, blank transparencies, overhead pens, transparency
of page 24; *Attribute Blocks*, student copies of page 24, colored cutouts of
page 20, paste

Warm-Up

Ask children to *sort* their sets of attribute blocks by *color*. Display this sorting
procedure using a limited assortment of small blocks. Have children follow
along with their blocks as you demonstrate the color sorting procedure on the
projector. Ask children how many colors there are. Then ask how many groups
they formed during the color sorting process. Follow this procedure to sort the
blocks by *size*, *shape*, and *thickness*.

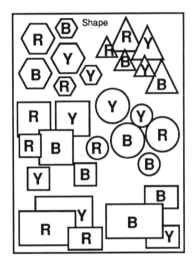

Activity

Shape Rodeo. (Sort into two groups) Children can do this activity with either a
set of large blocks or a set of small blocks and a copy of page 24. Display all the
small blocks around the edge of the projector glass. Ask children how they
would sort this set of blocks into only two groups. Then ask how they would
name the two groups. Several solutions are possible, such as *red* and *not red* or
circles and *not circles*. Naming one group of blocks with one attribute, such as
red, is simple; naming a multicolored or multisized group is not as obvious.
After the sorting procedure is finished, label each lasso with the appropriate
group name.

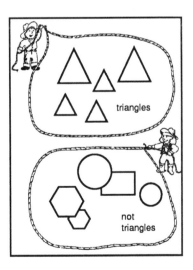

Practice

Have pairs of children find and record the results of a two-group sorting activity
by pasting colored cutouts of the attribute blocks on page 24. Have children label
the groups by printing the group names if they are able to.

Wrap-Up

Ask children to show and talk about the two groups they formed. Have them sort
objects such as pattern blocks or the *Three Bear Family™ Counters* into two
groups to reinforce the concept.

Shape Rodeo

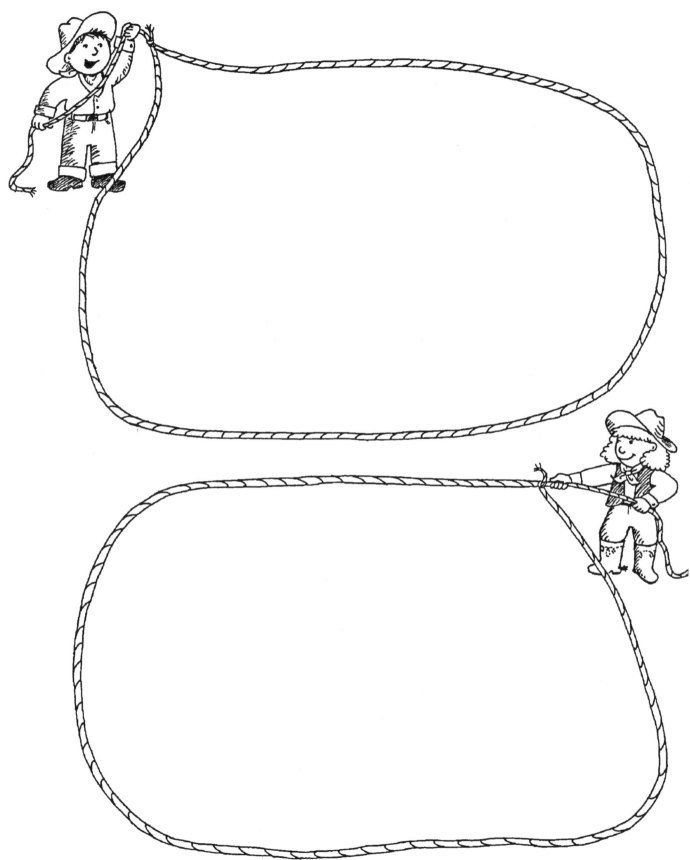

Patterns

✓ Objectives

To identify and copy patterns.
To substitute attributes in a pattern.

Vocabulary

pattern, copy, replace

Materials

Overhead Attribute Blocks, transparency of page 26; *Attribute Blocks*,
student copies of page 26, colored cutouts of page 20, paste, paper

Warm-Up

Copy and Create Patterns. Display some simple patterns on the overhead and
ask children to copy them with their sets of blocks. Shown at the right are an
ice cream cone, a rocket, a snowman, and a house. Have children work in pairs
to create and copy each other's patterns. Have them save their creations by
pasting cutouts of the attribute blocks on paper and then displaying them in
the classroom.

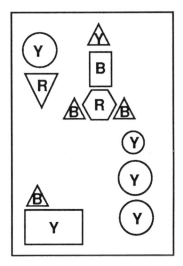

Activity

Patterns. Distribute page 26. Display the transparency of page 26 and ask
children to cover each block shown on the page with red blocks. Then ask them
to make the same pattern in yellow blocks (first column of dots). Finally, ask
them to make the pattern in blue blocks (second column of dots). You may also
ask them to replace each row of blocks with blocks of a different size or
thickness. Have them remove all the blocks for another activity. Now ask
children to cover each block with blue blocks. Then ask them to *replace* the
square and the triangle with yellow blocks. Ask if they can see a color pattern
that is beginning to form. Try other substitutions for color, size, and thickness.

Practice

Each child should have a 30-piece set of blocks and page 26. Place a
transparency of page 26 on the projector and keep the projector turned off. Keep
track of your directions as you give a set like this:

> **Cover all of the blocks on the page with red blocks.**
> **Replace all the four-sided blocks with blue blocks.**
> **Now replace the three-sided block with a yellow one.**
> **What does your pattern look like?** [red circle, blue square, blue
> rectangle, yellow triangle, red hexagon]

After several children have responded, turn on the projector to verify their
answers.

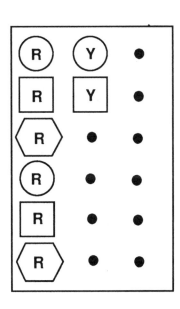

Wrap-Up

Have children work in pairs—one creates a simple one-color pattern and the
other copies it. Then have them make the same pattern using a different color,
shape, or size.

Patterns

Overhead Manipulatives in Action, K–3
© 1992 Learning Resources, Inc.

One-Way Change

 **Objectives**

To identify a one-attribute difference.
To sequence attribute blocks with successive one-attribute differences.

Vocabulary
one-way change

Materials
Overhead Attribute Blocks, blank transparency, overhead pen, transparency of page 28; *Attribute Blocks*, student copies of page 28, colored cutouts of blocks, paste, paper

Warm-Up
One-Way Change. Children should have a 30-piece set of attribute blocks. Place a large red hexagon on the projector. Ask children to find a **large red hexagon**. Then ask them to find a block that is different in only one way. Ask them what the *one-way change* is for each solution they present. Repeat with other blocks.

Activity
One-Way Change Sequences. Tell children that they are going to make special trains. Working individually or in pairs with their 30-piece set of attribute blocks, have children help complete the example you will demonstrate. Display a **large red square** on the projector. Ask students also to start with a large red square and follow along. Tell them the rule: *the next block must have a one-way change.* Ask for suggestions for the second block. Although there are seven possible second blocks, accept the first correct suggestion and then move on to the third block, which will also have several possibilities. Decide on the third and then the fourth block. For example, a one-way change train of four blocks can be large red square, large yellow square, small yellow square, small yellow triangle. Have children make one-way change trains of their own. Encourage them to record their sequence trains by pasting colored cutouts of the blocks on paper.

Practice
At the Fair. Working with their sets of attribute blocks and page 28, individuals or pairs must complete a one-way change sequence of four blocks on a merry-go-round. This activity is more difficult than the one above in that the first and fourth blocks must also have a one-way change. Direct children to follow the arrows on the merry-go-round shown on the page.

Wrap-Up
Have children show various ways they can complete the sequence of blocks on the merry-go-round.

Extension Activity
One-way change domino game. Pairs of children take turns placing dominoes in a line so that each block differs from the previous block in only one way.

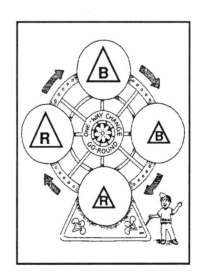

At the Fair

Attribute Blocks

(28)

Overhead Manipulatives in Action, K–3
© 1992 Learning Resources, Inc.

One-Two-Three Game

 Objectives

To identify two- and three- attribute differences.
To sequence attribute blocks with one-, two-, and three-attribute differences.

Vocabulary

two-way change, three-way change

Materials

Overhead Attribute Blocks, blank transparency, overhead pen, transparency of page 30, *Attribute Blocks*, student copies of page 30, colored cutouts of blocks, paste, paper

Warm-Up

Two-Way Change. Children should have a 30-piece set of attribute blocks for this activity. Place a *large red hexagon* on the projector. Direct children to find that piece from their set. Ask them to find a block that is different in two ways. Have them tell about the two-way change. Repeat this activity with other blocks. Then ask for a *three-way change.*

Activity

Two-Way and Three-Way Change Sequences. Have children make special "trains". They should have sets of attribute blocks as you demonstrate how to make a two-way change train. Start with a *large red square.* Tell them the rule: *the next block must be different in two ways.* Ask for possible solutions for the second block. Also have them tell how the block is different in two ways. Then direct children to find the third and fourth blocks of their trains. Have them make two-way change trains of their own. Encourage students to record their two-way change trains by pasting colored cutouts of the attribute blocks on a sheet of paper. Challenge some students to make three-way change trains.

Practice

One-Two-Three Game. Distribute page 30. Using their attribute blocks, children must complete the game by paying attention to the number of arrows between the large circles in the One–Two–Three Game. Play one game with the children using the overhead attribute blocks and page 30 on the projector.

Wrap-Up

Display children's solutions to the game on the overhead projector.

Extension

Two-Way Cover Up Game. Children will need a set of attribute blocks and paper. Have one player cover their eyes while his/her partner selects an attribute block and a corresponding attribute block that is different in two ways. Display the first block and cover the second block. Now ask the other player to look at the attribute block and try to figure out which block is covered. Make this game more challenging using three-way changes.

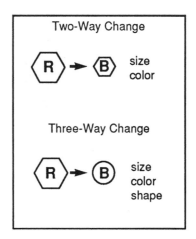

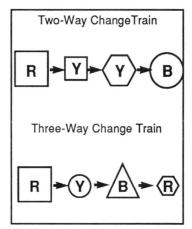

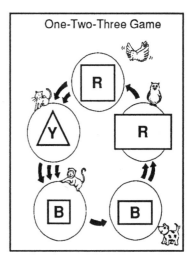

Attribute Blocks

One-Two-Three Game

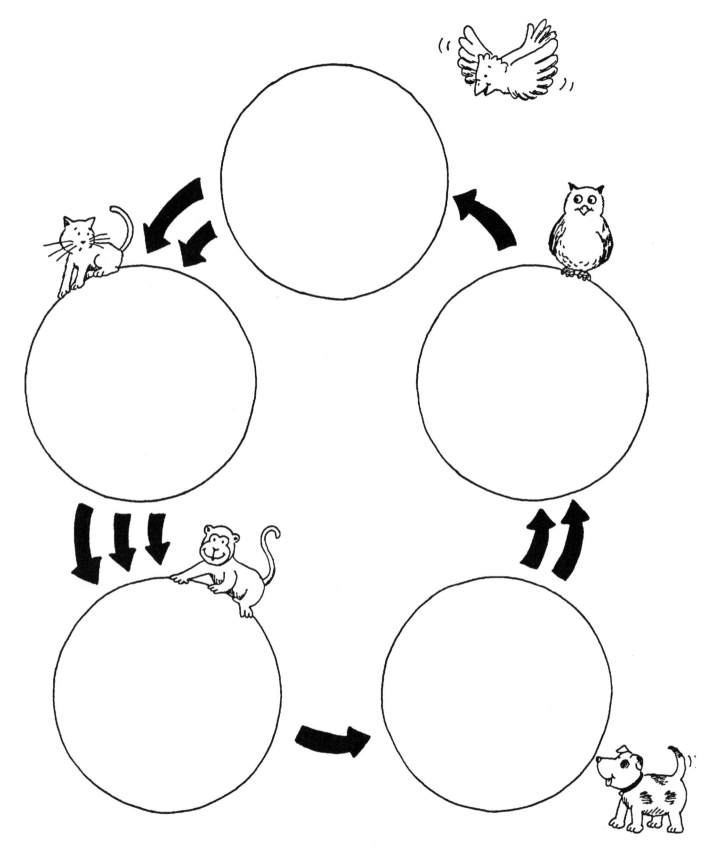

Overhead Manipulatives in Action, K–3
© 1992 Learning Resources, Inc.

More Shapes

 **Objectives**

To identify and describe geometric shapes.
To distinguish shapes from one another.

Vocabulary

square, rectangle, circle, hexagon, triangle, (parallelogram, trapezoid, rhombus, pentagon, octagon)

Materials

Overhead Attribute Blocks, both sets of *Shape Tracer Sets*, blank transparency, transparency of page 32, overhead pen; attribute blocks, student copies of page 32, pencils

Warm-Up

Same–Different. You will need a small set of attribute blocks in one color and a transparency of page 32. Focus on the attribute and Tracer shapes for this activity. Display the attribute block circle on the top of page 32 and the Tracer circle on the bottom portion. Ask: **Are these shapes the same or different?** [same] **How are they the same?** [They're round.] **Can you name the shapes?** [circle] Replace the Tracer circle with the ellipse. Then ask: **Are the shapes the same or different?** [different] **How are they different?** [One is round, the other is oval or egg shape.] **Can you name the shapes?** [circle, oval or ellipse]

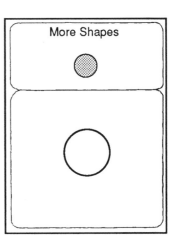

Activity

Continue the *Warm-Up* activity. Depending on the grade level and ability of the students, try these pairs or combinations of blocks:

Attribute Blocks	Tracer Shapes
square	square [same]; rhombus. rectangle, trapezoid [different]
rectangle	rectangle [same]; parallelogram, trapezoid, square, rhombus, kite [different]
triangle	equilateral triangle [same]; other Tracer triangles and shapes [different]
hexagon	hexagon [same]; pentagon, octagon, heptagon, other Tracer shapes [different]

Do not expect very young students to be able to identify each Tracer shape. Accept adequate descriptions and the identification of similarities and differences.

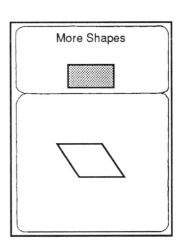

Practice

Have children make their own sets of Tracer shapes by tracing the shapes on colored construction paper and cutting them out. They can pair up and continue the *Warm-Up* and the *Activity* above.

Wrap-Up

Present problems similar to those in the *Warm-Up* on the projector.

More Shapes

Overhead Manipulatives in Action, K–3
© 1992 Learning Resources, Inc.

Pattern Blocks

Introduction

Overhead Pattern Blocks are especially effective for demonstrating explorations dealing with geometric shapes, visual spatialization, patterns, and symmetry. By using pattern blocks to create various shapes and mosaic designs, children also have the opportunity to gain an aesthetic as well as a quantitative appreciation for the blocks. The 49-piece pattern block set consists of six shapes in six colors—*orange square, green triangle, red trapezoid, yellow hexagon, blue parallelogram* and *white (clear) rhombus*. Younger children may refer to the parallelograms and rhombuses as "diamonds" at first. Gradually get them to use the correct geometric name for this shape. In the last lesson of this section, the children will also use the *Shape Tracer Sets* to explore the concept of symmetry.

Pattern Block Activities

 ## Getting Organized

Materials you will need:
- ◆ *Overhead Pattern Blocks* (LER 640)
- ◆ One transparency each of pages 36, 38, 40, 42, 44, 46
- ◆ *Shape Tracer Set* (LER 279) and *Shape Tracer Extension Set* (LER 280)
- ◆ Blank transparencies, overhead pens

Materials students will need:
- ◆ *Pattern Blocks* (Plastic LER 134, Wood LER 334)
- ◆ Copies of pages 34, 36, 38, 40, 42, 44, 46
- ◆ *Shape Tracer Set* (LER 279) and *Shape Tracer Extension Set* (LER 280)
- ◆ Crayons or color markers, scissors, paste, pencils, paper

 ## Getting Started

Introduce the pattern blocks by giving each child six blocks, one of each shape. If pattern blocks are not available, have children color and cut out the shapes shown on page 34. Allow children to manipulate the blocks to make various designs. Observe what children say and do. Compliment them on their knowledge of the colors and shapes of the blocks if they can identify the blocks correctly. After manipulating the blocks for a short time, some children may discover that all of the sides of each block are the same size (length) and that any two adjacent blocks can fit snugly together. Most children may be able to identify the colors (*orange, green, red, yellow, blue, white*), the sizes (*large, small*), and some of the shapes such as the square and the triangle.

Pattern Blocks

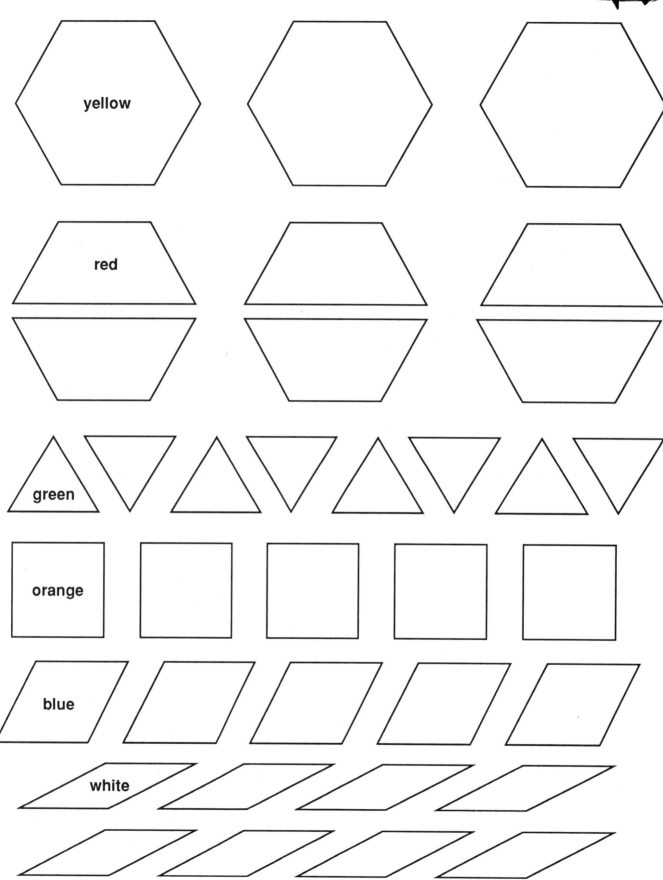

yellow

red

green

orange

blue

white

Overhead Manipulatives in Action, K–3
© 1992 Learning Resources, Inc.

Sort and Classify

 **Objective**

To sort and classify pattern blocks.

Vocabulary

sort, yellow, red, green, blue, orange, white, hexagon, trapezoid, triangle, square, rhombus, parallelogram

Materials

Overhead Pattern Blocks, transparency of page 36, overhead pens; *Pattern Blocks*, student copies of page 36

Warm-Up

Sort by Color. Give each pair of children a set of pattern blocks as noted below. Ask them to sort the blocks into groups by color. Ask:

> **How many groups are there?** [6] **How many colors are there?** [6]
> **How many blocks of each color?** [1 yellow, 2 red, 2 orange, 3 blue, 4 white, 6 green]
> **Can you name the shape for each color?**
> [yellow hexagons, orange squares, blue parallelograms, white rhombuses, green triangles]

Activity

Shape House. (Sort and classify by sides) Distribute page 36 and a set of pattern blocks to each pair. Display the transparency of page 36 on the projector along with the set of pattern blocks, one of each shape, around the edge. Tell children that the figure on page 36 is a three-story house and that they are going to store the blocks on different floors according to the number of sides. Ask children the following questions: **Are there are any blocks with three sides?** [yes] **Place the blocks with three sides on the top floor.** (pause) **What is the name of the shape with three sides?** [triangle] Repeat the procedure for the middle and bottom floors. **Are there any blocks with four sides?** [yes] **Place the blocks with four sides on the middle floor.** (pause) **What are the names of the four-sided blocks?** [squares, trapezoids, parallelograms, and rhombuses] **Are there any blocks with five sides?** [no] **Are there any blocks with six sides?** [yes] **What is the name of that block?** [hexagon] Depending on children's grade and/or ability level, you can write the shape words for them.

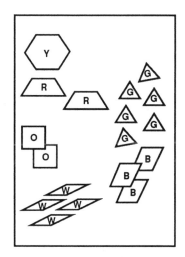

Practice

Working with an assortment of pattern blocks and page 36, direct children to sort and classify the pattern blocks by shape.

Wrap-Up

Call on children to describe the procedure they used for sorting the blocks. Ask them to name the shapes and colors in each group that resulted from the sorting procedure.

Shape House

Pattern Blocks

Overhead Manipulatives in Action, K–3
© 1992 Learning Resources, Inc.

Copies of Blocks

✓ Objective

To re-create a pattern block shape using other pattern blocks.
(To make *congruent* figures.)

Vocabulary

yellow, red, green, blue, orange, white, hexagon, trapezoid, triangle, square, rhombus, parallelogram

Materials

Overhead Pattern Blocks, transparency of page 38; *Pattern Blocks*, student copies of page 38, crayons or color markers, pencils

Warm-Up

Two-Block Shapes. Direct children to choose two blocks of the same shape and put them together. Ask if the new shape is a shape they can name, like a *parallelogram* or a *rectangle*. Discuss all of their shapes. Then ask them to make *three-block shapes*.

Activity

Copies of the Blocks. Distribute page 38, a set of pattern blocks, and a set of crayons and pencils. Display the transparency of page 38 on the projector. Read through the directions as you investigate each problem. **Look at problem 1. Place a blue block on BLUE. What shape is the blue block?** [rhombus or parallelogram] **Now find 2 blocks that will make that same shape.** [2 green triangles] Call on a child to describe the new shape. When all children have agreed that this is the only possible way to re-create the blue rhombus, say: **As you remove the blocks from these two shapes, draw lines and color the shapes of the blocks to record your answer.**

Follow the same procedure for problems 2 and 3. (The solutions are shown at the right.) Help children find one way to form the hexagon and then assign the rest of the page as independent work.

Practice

After children have found at least six ways to re-create the hexagon in problem 3, call on them to describe their solutions.

Wrap-Up

Depending on grade and ability level, you may wish to summarize the activity by telling students that they formed shapes *congruent* to the original pattern block shapes.

Extension Activity

Fractional Parts. After children have completed page 38 and colored in the color combinations of blocks for the pattern block, ask them about the fractional parts shown when smaller pattern blocks were used to make a large pattern block. For example, when the blue and green blocks are used to make the red trapezoid, 1/3 of the shape is now green and 2/3 of the shape is now blue.

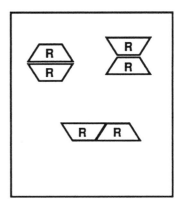

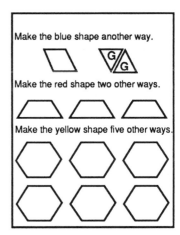

Make the blue shape another way.

Make the red shape two other ways.

Make the yellow shape five other ways.

Solutions:

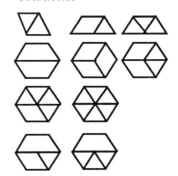

Pattern Blocks

Copies of Pattern Blocks

1. Make the blue shape another way.

BLUE

2 blocks

2. Make the red shape two other ways.

RED   2 blocks   3 blocks

3. Make the yellow shape five other ways.

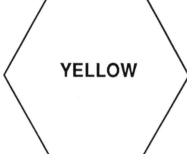
YELLOW   2 blocks   3 blocks

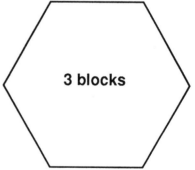
4 blocks   5 blocks   6 blocks

Overhead Manipulatives in Action, K–3
© 1992 Learning Resources, Inc.

Larger Block Shapes

✓ Objective

To re-create pattern block shapes in larger sizes.
(To make *similar* figures.)

Vocabulary

yellow, red, green, blue, orange, white, hexagon, trapezoid, triangle, square, rhombus, parallelogram

Materials

Overhead Pattern Blocks, transparency of page 40; *Pattern Blocks*, student copies of page 40, colored cutouts of pattern block shapes (page 34), paste

Warm-Up

Larger Triangles. Display a green triangle on the projector. Ask children to use their blocks to make a large triangle of the same shape. (There are many possibilities, two of which are shown at the right.) Repeat this activity for making a larger square.

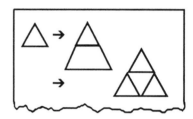

Activity

Larger Pattern Blocks. Distribute page 40 to each child and a set of pattern blocks to each group of two or three. Point to the trapezoid on the page. Ask children to find at least one solution for making that shape. Call on various children to share their solutions with the class. (A few solutions are shown at the lower right.)

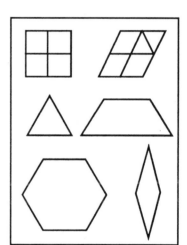

Practice

Assign the rest of page 40 as independent class work. Direct children to paste colored cutouts of the pattern blocks on the enlarged figures to show at least one solution per shape. Give children several copies of page 40 in order to show many solutions for making the larger block shapes.

Wrap-Up

After children have formed all the shapes on page 40, ask them to use a pattern block to check that all the angles (corners) are still the same size as the original pattern block. When the angle remains the same measure as the sides increase (or decrease) proportionately, then a *similar* figure has been formed.

Sample Solutions:

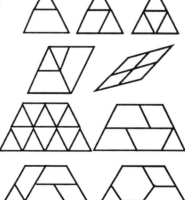

Extension Activity

Encourage some children to enlarge the pattern block shapes to enormous proportions, perhaps making a trapezoid as large as a sheet of paper or the desktop.

Large Pattern Blocks

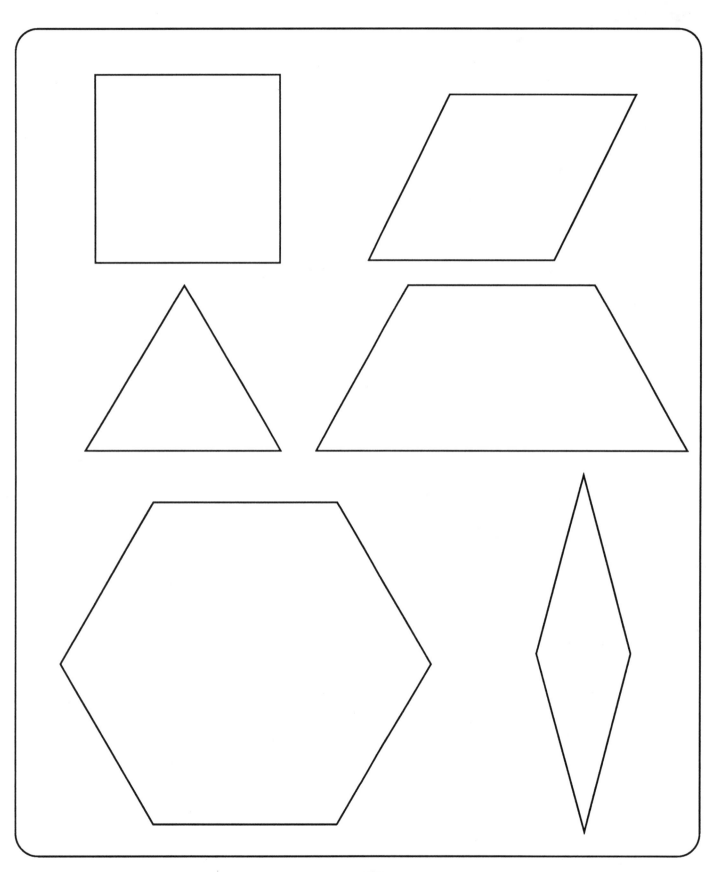

Overhead Manipulatives in Action, K–3
© 1992 Learning Resources, Inc.

Copy Cat

 **Objectives**

To copy a given design.
To increase visual memory skills.

Vocabulary
copy, design

Materials
Overhead Pattern Blocks, transparency of page 42; *Pattern Blocks*, student copies of page 42, colored cutouts of the blocks on page 34, paste

Warm-Up
Display a simple design made with four or five pattern blocks on the projector. Ask children to copy it. Then ask a volunteer to come to the projector to copy the design using the overhead pattern blocks.

Activity
Copy Cat Game. Distribute pattern blocks to each pair of children and page 42 to each child. Have one child create a mosaic design and the other child copy it. Have them continue to take turns creating and copying designs.

Practice
Have students make permanent copies of their designs by pasting colored cutouts of the pattern blocks onto page 42. Treat these completed sheets as design cards for the entire class to exchange and copy.

Wrap-Up
Ask questions about all the wonderful designs that were made. Point out the aesthetic qualities of the designs as well as the mathematical and geometric aspects. It is important that children gain an appreciation for the color and balance of the design in addition to the shape and number of blocks used.

Extension Activity
Two teams of four, one team at each table, are needed for this activity. Direct one team to make an elaborate mosaic design with the pattern blocks, using one or more sets. Then have the other team copy the design.

Copy Cat

Overhead Manipulatives in Action, K–3
© 1992 Learning Resources, Inc.

Exploring Symmetry

 **Objective**

To find all lines of symmetry for each pattern block.

Vocabulary

fold line, symmetry, symmetric

Materials

Overhead Pattern Blocks, transparency of page 44; cutouts of pattern blocks for teacher and students, overhead pens; *Pattern Blocks*, student copies of page 44, pencils, scissors, colored paper

Warm-Up

Give each child a sheet of colored paper and scissors. Direct children to fold the paper in half and then cut out a heart or a pine tree. Demonstrate by folding and cutting out a heart. When the heart is unfolded, there is a line in the middle of it and each portion of the heart on each side of the line is exactly the same size.

Activity

Exploring Symmetry. (Symmetry of each pattern block) You and your students need a set of cutouts shown on page 34 in addition to the set of pattern blocks. Distribute page 44. Place the transparency of page 44 on the projector. Tell children that they are going to find out if the pattern blocks can be folded so that one half will cover the other half. Tell them that the fold line is a *line of symmetry* for the shape. For example, have students look at the red trapezoid and ask them to think about whether the trapezoid has a line of symmetry. After some discussion, ask children to see if they can fold the paper cutout of the trapezoid in half. Then ask them to record the fold line on the trapezoid on page 44. Ask if they can fold the trapezoid in half in another way to find another line of symmetry. Since the trapezoid contains only one line of symmetry, go on to another pattern block shape such as the square. Ask children to fold the shape and then to record the fold lines on the square on page 44.

Practice

Continue the activity as independent class work until children have found the lines of symmetry for all six shapes.

Wrap-Up

Ask children to share their results. Ask them to list the pattern blocks with only one line of symmetry, then two lines of symmetry, and so on.

Extension Activity

Symmetry of Pattern Block Designs. Direct children to use their creativity to make a pattern block design and then find all the lines of symmetry for it.

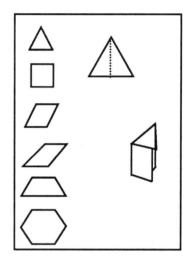

Solutions:

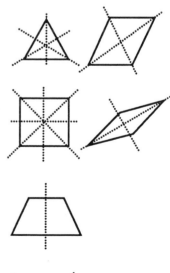

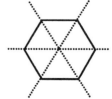

Exploring Symmetry

Pattern Blocks

Overhead Manipulatives in Action, K–3
© 1992 Learning Resources, Inc.

Symmetry of Other Shapes

 Objective

To find lines of symmetry of geometric shapes.

Vocabulary

square, rectangle, pentagon, hexagon, octagon, circle, equilateral triangle, isosceles triangle, ellipse, predict

Materials

Shape Tracer Set, transparency of page 46; student copies of pages 46, two colors of pencils, paper, scissors

Warm-Up

Distribute page 46. Ask children if they recognize any of the shapes. Ask if they can tell you which ones are Attribute Block shapes [square, rectangle, hexagon, equilateral triangle, circle] or Pattern Block shapes. [square, equilateral triangle, hexagon] Discuss the characteristics of each shape. Talk about the remaining shapes—(isosceles triangle, pentagon, octagon, ellipse).

Activity

Shape Symmetry. Distribute page 46. Ask children to predict the lines of symmetry for each *Shape Tracer Set* shape and then to show the lines of symmetry with a colored pencil. Some of the shapes (square, equilateral triangle, hexagon) were investigated for lines of symmetry in the previous lesson. Ask students whether the isosceles triangle will have three lines of symmetry just as the equilateral triangle did. Ask about the lines of symmetry for a circle. Ask if the rectangle will contain as many lines of symmetry as the square.

Practice

Let children work in cooperative groups of four. Have them trace and cut out the *Shape Tracer Set* shapes and then fold them to find the lines of symmetry of each shape. Direct children to mark the actual lines of symmetry on page 46 using a regular pencil. Have them observe the difference in their predictions and the actual lines of symmetry found during this activity.

Wrap-Up

Ask children to make general statements regarding the lines of symmetry of geometric shapes and also about particular situations. For example:
Does a shape have more lines of symmetry if it is a regular polygon than if it is an irregular polygon? How many lines of symmetry does a circle have?

Extension Activity

Have children find the lines of symmetry for the shapes in the *Tracer Extension Set.*

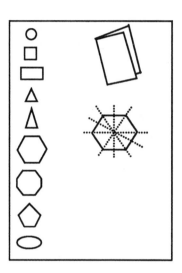

Solutions:

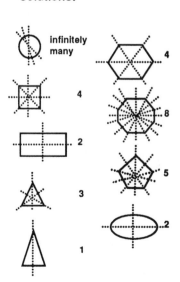

Shape Symmetry

Show the lines of symmetry.

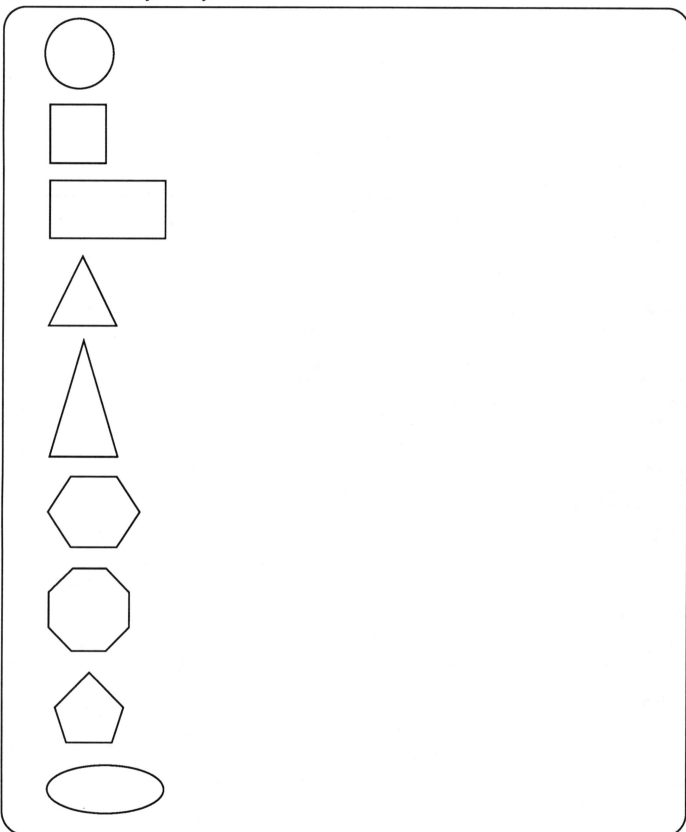

Overhead Manipulatives in Action, K–3
© 1992 Learning Resources, Inc.

Numbers 1–100

Introduction

Using the set of *Numbers 1–100* children are able to move numbers around freely in order to find a solution or several solutions. Because of this mobility, children develop a more venturesome attitude for making numerical guesses and then experimenting with the number squares. Although there are many ways to use the set of *Numbers 1–100*, the lessons that follow focus on numerals associated with sets of objects, various forms of counting, and investigating numeration concepts and patterns. Students will also develop number sense by finding the largest and smallest solutions for a given number of digits.

Numbers 1–100 Activities

 ## Getting Organized

Materials you will need:
- ◆ *Overhead Numbers 1–100* (LER 378)
- ◆ *Transparent Counters* (LER 131)
- ◆ *Overhead Color Squares* (LER 478)
- ◆ One transparency each of pages 50, 52, 54, 56, 58, 60
- ◆ Blank transparencies, overhead pens

Note: You may wish to store the numbers in four plastic ziplock bags—1–25, 26–50, 51–75, 76–100—for easy retrieval.

- ◆ *Number Squares 1–100* (LER 381)
- ◆ *Transparent Counters* (LER 131)
- ◆ *Color Cubes, MathLink™ Cubes* or similar linking cubes
- ◆ Copies of pages 48, 50, 52, 54, 56, 58, 60
- ◆ Scissors, pencils, paper

You can use page 48 to make the set of *Numbers 1–100*, or you can use it as a hundred board. Duplicating page 48 on brightly colored paper will make the numbers more appealing to students.

 ## Getting Started

When using the set of *Numbers 1–100* with kindergarten students, use only the numbers that children are familiar with such as 1–5, 1–10, or even 1–20. Students in the latter part of first grade and second graders can be given the entire set of numbers. As with other manipulatives, allow children a short time to play with the set of *Number Squares 1–100*. Children have probably not had an opportunity to handle numbers before in this manner. Watch what they do during this free time—lining up the numbers from 1 through 100 in one very long line across a table or finding all the tens. Although plastic sets of numbers may be available for use with the activities on pages 49–60, children should have their own set of *Numbers 1–100* (page 48) for use with any mathematics lesson.

Numbers 1–100

1	2	3	4	5	6	7	8	9	10
11	12	13	14	15	16	17	18	19	20
21	22	23	24	25	26	27	28	29	30
31	32	33	34	35	36	37	38	39	40
41	42	43	44	45	46	47	48	49	50
51	52	53	54	55	56	57	58	59	60
61	62	63	64	65	66	67	68	69	70
71	72	73	74	75	76	77	78	79	80
81	82	83	84	85	86	87	88	89	90
91	92	93	94	95	96	97	98	99	100

Overhead Manipulatives in Action, K–3
© 1992 Learning Resources, Inc.

Sets and Numerals

 Objective

To associate a numeral with a set of objects.

Vocabulary

number, numeral

Materials

Overhead Numbers 1–100, Transparent Counters, transparency of page 50, sheet of paper; *Number Squares 1–100*, counters for student use, student copies of page 60 (optional: crayons, markers, stickers, rubber stamps of shapes)

Warm-Up

Initiate a discussion about numbers. Tell children to think of places where numbers are used. Ask them to find numbers in the classroom.

Activity

Sets and Numerals. Distribute number squares 1–10, 10 or 12 counters, and page 50. Display a transparency of page 50 on the projector. (There are two ways to present this activity—show a number tile and ask for the corresponding number of counters, or show a set of counters and ask for the corresponding number tile.) Cover the transparency so that only the bear is visible. Place four counters next to the bear. Ask children to count the counters. Then ask them to find the number square for the number of counters. [4] Move the paper down to uncover the rabbit. Put the number tile 5 in the rabbit's square. Direct children to place that number of counters next to the rabbit. Ask: **What is the number? How many counters did you put next to the rabbit? Can you count them aloud for me one by one?** Continue the activity for the bird and the elephant.

Practice

Working in pairs, children can challenge each other to show the correct number of counters or the correct numeral. For example, one child selects a number tile and the partner must place the correct number of counters for that numeral. In this way, one child can get instant feedback from the other. Play ten rounds. Children may wish to make a permanent copy of their work by drawing figures, rubber-stamping figures, or attaching stickers to correspond to the numerals written in the squares.

Wrap-Up

Call on children one by one to provide the correct number of counters for a numeral or to provide the correct numeral (number square) for a given set of counters.

Extension Activity

Have children use other counters such as the *Three Bear Family™ Counters* or coins.

Sets and Numerals

Overhead Manipulatives in Action, K–3
© 1992 Learning Resources, Inc.

Count On, Count Back

 **Objective**

To count on or count back from a given number.

Vocabulary

count on, count back

Materials

Overhead Numbers 1–100, *Transparent Counters*, transparency of page 52; *Number Squares 1–100*, counters for student use, student copies of page 52 (Note: Cut the transparency of page 52 in half if you wish to focus on *counting on* at one time and *counting back* at another time.)

Warm-Up

Distribute a set of number squares to each pair of children. Direct them to put the numbers in order from 1 to 100. Two children can complete this activity very quickly and also check on each other's sequencing.

Activity

Count On, Count Back. Distribute page 52. Children can work in pairs with a set of number squares or they can work individually with their own set of numbers 1–100. Select a number, say, 38, and place it in the bird's box. Direct children to find the next three numbers in the sequence; that is, *count on* from 38. With children of lesser ability, you may wish to start with 1 or a very small number. Continue the counting on activity until most children can quickly complete the sequences. Challenge the students to count on by twos, threes, or fives from a given number. Try the same activity for *counting back* using the bottom part of page 52. Counting on and counting back are valuable skills that are needed for finding sums and differences quickly as well as to count money and make change.

Practice

Have children work in pairs to continue the activity. One child selects a number and the other counts on or counts back.

Wrap-Up

After children have completed several counting on and counting back exercises, ask them what the largest number can be in the first counting on box if the last number in the sequence is 100. Likewise, ask children what the smallest number must be in the last counting back box if the first number in the sequence is 1.

Count On, Count Back

Overhead Manipulatives in Action, K–3
© 1992 Learning Resources, Inc.

Count and Compare

Objectives

To count objects in a given set.
To associate a numeral with a given set of objects.
To compare two given numbers.

Vocabulary

equals, more than, less than

Materials

Overhead Numbers 1–100, Transparent Counters, transparency of page 54,
overhead pens; *Number Squares 1–100*, counters for student use, student copies
of page 54, pencils

Warm-Up

Ask children to think about the comparison of objects in the classroom. Ask:
**Which do you think is heavier, the chair or the globe? Who do you think is
taller, Mary or Jan? Are there more books on the top shelf or the middle
shelf?** The object of this informal activity is to put children into a comparison
frame of mind. Actual measurements do not have to be performed, only a
rational discussion is necessary.

Activity

Count and Compare. Distribute page 54, a set of numbers 1–100, and some
counters to each pair of children. Place the transparency of page 54 on the
projector. Also place some counters on each clown. Tell children that these two
clowns have bouncing polka dots on their clown suits. Ask them to count the
polka dots on each clown. (You may wish to have children estimate the number
before counting.) Ask a volunteer to come to the projector to count the counters.
Have children put the same number of counters on their clown figures so that
they can follow along for the rest of the activity. Ask them if they think one
clown has more polka dots than the other. And if it does, how many more polka
dots. Ask them how they could verify their convictions. Children might suggest
thinking of the sequence of numbers or showing a one-to-one correspondence.
Show the one-to-one correspondence (matching) of the counters for the two
clowns. If the number is the same for both clowns, then one quantity *equals* the
other quantity. If one clown has more (fewer) counters than the other clown, then
one quantity is *less than* (*more than*) the other quantity. Introduce the symbols =,
< , and > in subsequent examples.

Practice

Go around the room placing a small handful of counters on each child's
clowns. Have children count and compare the clowns' polka dots. Do this
activity several times.

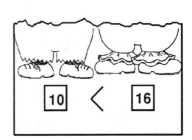

Wrap-Up

Direct children to look closely at the number squares associated with the sets of
polka dots. Ask about the size and placement of the digits in the numerals used.

Count and Compare

Overhead Manipulatives in Action, K–3
© 1992 Learning Resources, Inc.

Even or Odd

 **Objective**

To investigate even and odd numbers.

Vocabulary

even, odd

Materials

Overhead Numbers 1–100, *Overhead Color Squares*, transparency of page 56, overhead pens, blank transparency; *Number Squares 1–100*, square counters or colored cubes for student use, student copies of page 56, pencils

Warm-Up

Lead children in a choral counting exercise. Have them snap their figures for fives and clap their hands for tens during a counting exercise from 1–50. Ask them to count by twos from 2. Then ask them to think about the twos. What digit does a two always have as its last digit?

Activity

Even and Odd. Distribute square counters or colored cubes, such as MathLink™ or Unifix Cubes, and page 56. Place the transparency of page 56 on the projector, place a number square, say 26, in the bear's box, and ask: **How do I know if this is an even number or an odd number?** Then show children this example: Fill the rows of squares with 26 color squares. Notice that there are no single squares left over. Therefore, 26 is an *even* number. Try another example, using an *odd* number.

Practice

Working in pairs, have children choose a number for each other. Then have each child build the number to see if it is even or odd. You may wish to work with numbers up to 40 at first since there are only 42 squares on page 56. For larger numbers, children can show the pattern off the page. Remind children to record whether their numbers were even or odd in the space at the top of the page.

Wrap-Up

Ask every child for the numbers he or she worked with. Make a list on projector or the chalkboard of the children's result. Summarize the results:

◆ numbers ending in 0, 2, 4, 6, or 8 are even numbers because squares representing them can be arranged in two rows with no squares left over.

◆ numbers ending in 1, 3, 5, 7, and 9 are odd numbers.

Challenge children with numbers such as 136 or 467 or even 7,504.

Even or Odd

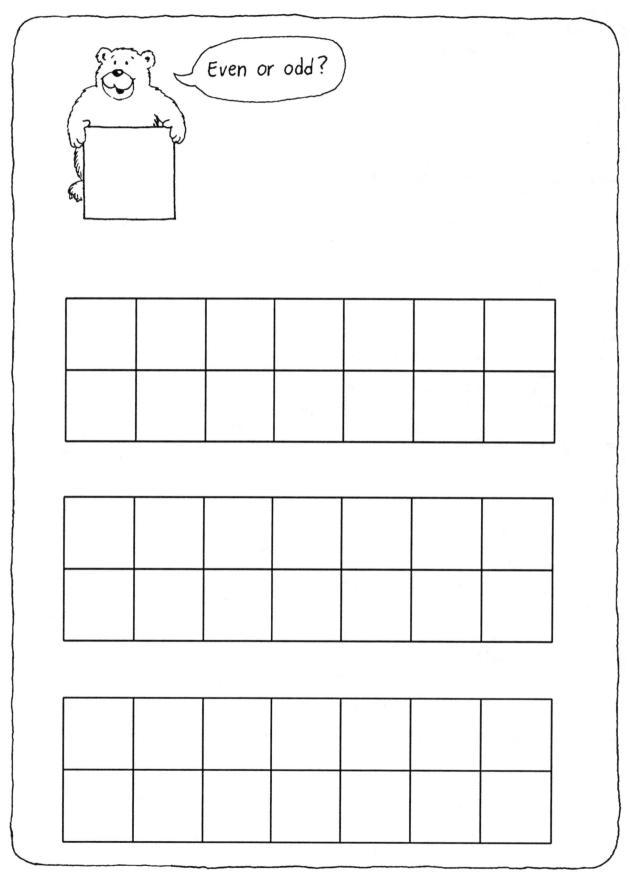

Overhead Manipulatives in Action, K–3
© 1992 Learning Resources, Inc.

Number Patterns

✓ Objective
To identify and extend number patterns.

Vocabulary
pattern

Materials
Overhead Numbers 1–100, transparency of page 58, overhead pens, blank transparency; *Number Squares 1–100*, student copies of page 58, pencils

Warm-Up
Do some quick rounds of counting on and counting back exercises with children. You may wish to retrieve page 52 for this warm-up activity.

Activity
Number Patterns. Distribute page 58 and a set of number squares. Suggest that children arrange their number squares in a line or on a 10 × 10 grid (hundred board) to help them find the number squares quickly for each problem. Show an obviously simple number pattern in the first five squares at the top. For example, use 12, 15, 18, 21, 24. Ask children about the numbers: **Are the numbers even? Are the numbers odd? Do they increase by a certain number each time? What do you think the next number is? The next? The next?**
[They increase by three each time; the next three numbers in the sequence are 27, 30, and 33.] Next, try number sequences like these: 7, 8, 10, 13, 17, 22 [28, 35, 43]; 1, 4, 9, 16, 25 [36, 49, 64]; 1, 4, 3, 6, 5, 8. [7, 10, 9]. Discuss each number pattern with the students.

Practice
Have children work in pairs or small cooperative groups of three or four to devise various number patterns for other groups to solve. Observe children as they move around the number squares to think of a problem or to solve a problem. Children should record their patterns on page 58 to share later with the class.

Wrap-Up
Discuss children's number patterns. Ask how it felt to move around numbers rather than write them down each time they had an idea. Ask if they tried more possibilities for the solution using the number squares rather than writing the numbers.

Number Patterns

Hop to it! Find the next three numbers.

Overhead Manipulatives in Action, K–3
© 1992 Learning Resources, Inc.

The Largest, the Smallest

 Objectives

To find the largest possible solution for three given digits in a problem.
To find the smallest possible solution for three given digits in a problem.
To reinforce place value knowledge about numbers.
To enhance computational estimation skills.

Vocabulary

add, addend, sum, subtract, difference, factor, product, divisor, dividend, quotient, largest, smallest, solution

Materials

Overhead Numbers 1–9, transparency of page 60, overhead pens, blank transparency; *Number Squares 1–9*, student copies of page 60, pencils

Warm-Up

Each child needs number squares 1–9 and paper. Display two digits on the projector. Ask children to give the largest and then the smallest two-digit number for them. After working with two-digit numbers for a while, show three digits and ask for the largest and the smallest possible three-digit numbers that can be formed from them. Show four or more digits if children are able to work with larger numbers.

Activity

The Largest, the Smallest. Distribute page 60 and a set of number squares 1–9. Display the transparency of page 60 on the projector with a blank transparency over it. Put the number squares 3, 7, and 8 in the three square boxes at the top of the page. Direct children to place the same three digits on the page. Then tell children that they are to fill in the problems with these three digits to make the largest possible solution for each problem. Circle the word *Largest* at the top of the page. For the *addition* problem, ask what kind of problem it is and how they could make the largest possible *sum* for two *addends* using 3, 7, and 8. Where would the digits be positioned and why? Have children make estimates and move around the digits on the page. They can use calculators to verify their predictions.

Practice

Ask children to find the smallest possible solutions for the digits 3, 7 and 8. Repeat the exercise using other digits.

Wrap-Up

When discussing children's results, make it a point to focus on the terminology associated with operations problems a well as finding the solutions.

The Largest, the Smallest

LARGEST   **SMALLEST**

☐ ☐ ☐

☐ ☐   ☐ ☐

\+ ☐   − ☐
_____   _____

☐ ☐

✕ ☐   ☐)☐ ☐
_____

Overhead Manipulatives in Action, K–3
© 1992 Learning Resources, Inc.

Base Ten Blocks

Introduction

Base Ten Blocks are especially useful for teaching place value of whole numbers and demonstrating the algorithms for addition, subtraction, multiplication, and division. In grades K through 3, the focus will be on place value, regrouping, and addition and subtraction involving two-digit numbers.

Base Ten Activities

 ## Getting Organized

Materials you will need:
- ◆ *Overhead Base Ten Blocks* (LER 650)
- ◆ *Overhead Numbers 1–100* (LER 378)
- ◆ *Transparent Spinners* (LER 158)
- ◆ One transparency each of pages 62, 63, 64, 66, 68, 70, 72, 74, 76
- ◆ Blank transparencies, overhead pens, sheet of paper

Materials students will need:
- ◆ *Base Ten Blocks* (plastic or wood)
- ◆ *Number Squares 1–100* (LER 381)
- ◆ *Transparent Spinners* (LER 158)
- ◆ Copies of pages 62, 63, 64, 66, 68, 70, 72, 74, 76
- ◆ Scissors, pencils, small paper clips

Duplicate page 62 on brightly colored paper. The place value mat on page 63 can be used with any place value activity.

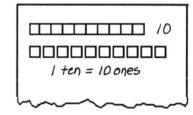

1 ten = 10 ones

 ## Getting Started

Permit children to explore with the *Base Ten Blocks* for a few minutes before starting formal activities. Introduce each type of block one at a time. Display the *ones* block. Ask children to pick up some ones blocks and show them to you. Next, introduce the *tens* block. Say: **This is a *tens* block. Why do you think it's called a tens block? Can you show how 10 ones is the same as 1 ten?** Direct children to put down a tens block and count aloud by tens in a choral response 10, 20, 30, ... until they get to 100. Model this activity by placing each tens block directly under a previous tens block to eventually form a hundreds block. Then ask: **Can you find a block that is as big as 10 tens blocks?** (pause) **Hold it up to show it to me. This is a *hundreds* block. Why do you think it is called a hundreds block?** [100 ones in 100] **Can you cover the hundreds block with 100 ones?** Wrap-up the activity by eliciting the following conclusions: 1 ten = 10 ones; 1 hundred = 100 ones; 1 hundred = 10 tens.

10 tens = 100

1, 2, 3...

100 ones = 100

Base Ten Blocks

Ones

Tens

Ones

Hundred

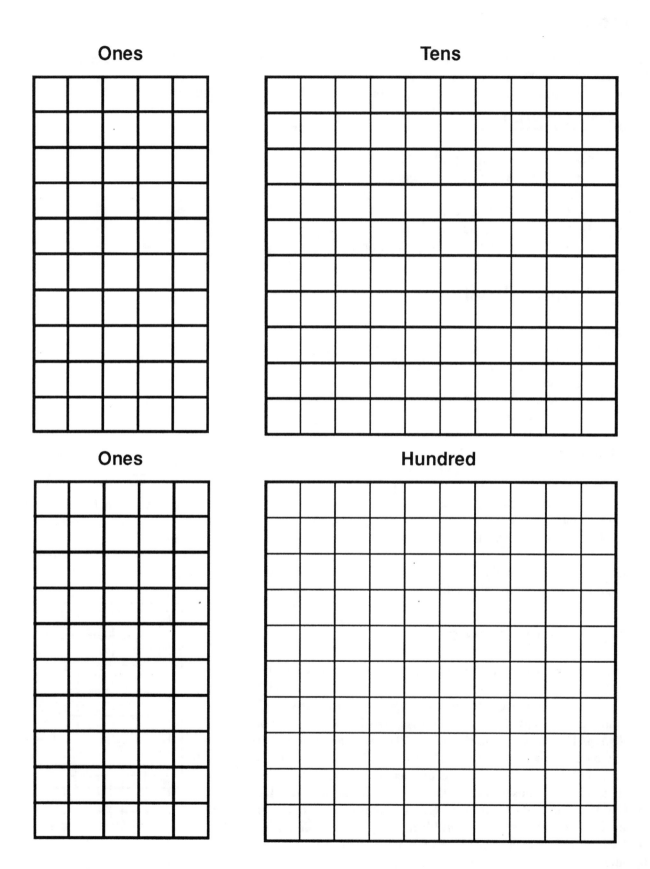

Overhead Manipulatives in Action, K–3
© 1992 Learning Resources, Inc.

Place Value Mat

TENS	ONES

Overhead Manipulatives in Action, K–3
© 1992 Learning Resources, Inc.

Base Ten Blocks

Tens and Ones

_____ tens _____ ones

_____ tens _____ ones

Numbers for Blocks

✓ Objective

To determine the number for a given set of base ten blocks.

Vocabulary

number, tens, ones

Materials

Overhead Base Ten Blocks, transparency of page 66, blank transparency, sheet of paper, overhead pens; *Base Ten Blocks*, student copies of page 66, pencils

Warm-Up

Direct children to count quickly by ones from 1 through 10, holding up the appropriate number of fingers for each number of the count. Quickly count by tens to 100 this way: Ask ten children to come to the front of the room. Have each child say a ten and show both hands of ten fingers. Then ask volunteers to count all the individual fingers for the ten children.

Activity

Numbers for Blocks. Distribute base ten blocks (preferably 9 tens and 9 ones) and page 66. Place the transparency of page 66 on the projector, covering the bottom portion of it with a sheet of paper. Turn on the projector and proceed as follows as children follow along with their set of base ten blocks. Display 1 ten and 4 ones blocks as shown. Ask:

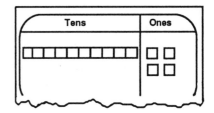

How many tens blocks are there? [1]
How many ones blocks are there? [4]
How many ones altogether? [14]

Remove the paper from page 66. Ask the same questions, this time recording the responses in the appropriate blanks and boxes shown on the page. Repeat the activity using other two-digit numbers.

Practice

Direct children to work in pairs to practice finding the number for a given set of tens and ones blocks. Have one child place some blocks on the top of the page while the partner figures out the number for the blocks and records it on the bottom portion of the page. If children use sets of number squares 1–100 in the blanks and the box at the bottom of the page, then they will not have to erase or scratch out previous responses.

Wrap-Up

Children should come to the following conclusion: In a two-digit number, the digit for the number of tens is recorded to the left of the digit for the number of ones.

Extension Activity

Try this activity using play dimes and pennies or $10 and $1 bills.

Numbers for Blocks

TENS	ONES

_____ tens _____ ones

Base Ten Blocks

Overhead Manipulatives in Action, K–3
© 1992 Learning Resources, Inc.

Blocks for Numbers

 **Objective**

To show a number using base ten blocks.

Vocabulary

number, tens, ones

Materials

Overhead Base Ten Blocks, Overhead Numbers 1–100, transparency of page 68, blank transparency, sheet of paper; *Base Ten Blocks*, student copies of page 68, *Number Squares 1–100*

Warm-Up

Play the Number Flash Game using the overhead numbers 1–100. Tell children you are going to show a number on the projector for only a few seconds. When you turn off the projector, ask some children what number they saw. Turn the projector back on to verify their responses, then show another number. Do 10 to 12 numbers in quick succession.

Activity

Blocks for Numbers. Distribute base ten blocks and page 68. Place the transparency of page 68 on the projector, covering the bottom part of the page. Insert an overhead number square in the box shown on the page. Ask:

> **What is the number?** [37]
> **What does the 3 stand for?** [3 tens]
> (or **In which place is the 3?** [tens place])
> **What does the 7 stand for?** [7 ones]
> (or **In which place is the 7?** [ones place])
> **Can you show this number using base ten blocks?**

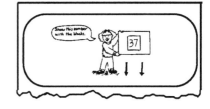

Remove the sheet of paper from the page. After children have finished this task on their own paper, ask a volunteer to come to the overhead projector to show the appropriate number of tens and ones blocks for 37.

Practice

Working in cooperative groups of four, have children put a set of number squares in a bag and then randomly choose a number square. That number square is the number to be represented by base ten blocks on page 68. When all children have their blocks displayed, direct group members to check one another's blocks. Repeat this activity several times.

Wrap-Up

Do the practice activity at the projector. Have one child choose a number square from a bag and then show the appropriate number of blocks on the projector. Repeat with several children.

Extension Activity

Try this activity using play money dimes and pennies or $10 and $1 bills.

Blocks for Numbers

TENS	ONES

Overhead Manipulatives in Action, K–3
© 1992 Learning Resources, Inc.

Trade Up

 Objective

To regroup ones for tens.

Vocabulary
number, tens, ones, regroup (trade)

Materials
Overhead Base Ten Blocks, Transparent Spinner, transparencies of pages 64 and 70; *Base Ten Blocks*, student copies of pages 64 and 70, *Transparent Spinners* or paper clips and pencils to make spinners

Warm-Up
Distribute base ten blocks and page 64. Place the transparency of page 64 on the projector, showing 13 ones blocks at the top of the page. Ask: **How many ones?** [13] **How many tens?** [0] **How can you show this number of ones another way with the blocks?** [1 ten, 3 ones] When children explain how they traded a ten for 10 ones, show this *regrouping* (trade) procedure on the overhead with the blocks. Repeat this activity using 4 tens and 18 ones, 3 tens and 23 ones, and so on. Be sure children understand that the simplest way (fewest number of blocks) to show a number is when there is a digit of 9 or less in the ones place.

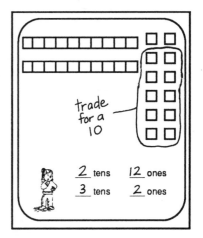

Activity
Trade Up. Play the Nifty Fifty Game. Distribute the materials, and place the transparency of page 70 on the projector. Put the transparent spinner over the circle with numbers 1–6. (If children do not have spinners, make spinners using outstretched paper clips and pencils.) Read the directions for the game and then demonstrate it with children following along. Pretend that you are both players. When there is a trade to be made, have a child come to the projector to help you. The object of the game is to be the first player to reach fifty (5 tens).

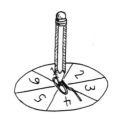

Practice
Have children decide whether they want to play in pairs, trios, or groups of four. Suggest that they put all of their base ten blocks in a central area for all to use during the game. Each child should have page 70. Observe children as they play the game.

Wrap-Up
Ask children what they did every time there were more than 9 ones in the ones place. Make sure all children can hear one another and share their experiences about the regrouping procedure.

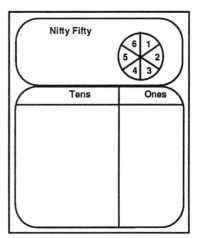

Extension Activity
Play the Nifty Fifty Game using play money dimes and pennies or $10 and $1 bills.

Trade Up

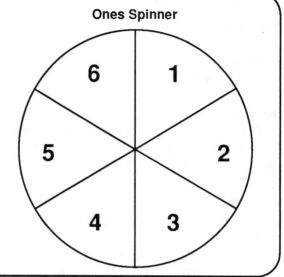

Nifty Fifty

Ones Spinner

Players: 2 or more

Materials: 5 tens blocks, 20 ones blocks per player, transparent spinner or paper clip and pencil

How to play: Take turns spinning the spinner and placing the appropriate number of ones on the mat. When there are 10 or more ones, trade them for a ten and some ones. When a player has 4 tens and some ones, spin until the exact number of ones makes 50 or lose a turn.

How to win: Be the first player to make 50!

TENS	ONES

Overhead Manipulatives in Action, K–3
© 1992 Learning Resources, Inc.

Trade Down

 **Objective**

To regroup tens for ones.

Vocabulary
number, tens, ones, regroup (trade)

Materials
Overhead Base Ten Blocks, Transparent Spinner, transparencies of pages 64 and 72; *Base Ten Blocks*, student copies of pages 64 and 72, *Transparent Spinners* or paper clips and pencils to make spinners

Warm-Up
Distribute base ten blocks and page 64. Place the transparency of page 64 on the projector, showing 4 tens and 3 ones blocks at the top of the page. Ask: **How many ones?** [3] **How many tens?** [4] **How can you show this number another way with one fewer tens block?** [3 tens, 13 ones] When children explain how they traded a ten for 10 ones, show this *regrouping* (trade) procedure on the overhead with the blocks. Repeat this activity using 5 tens and 6 ones, 6 tens and 0 ones, and so on.

Activity
Trade Down. Play the Wipe Out Game. Distribute the materials, then place the transparency of page 72 on the projector. Put the transparent spinner over the circle with numbers 1–6. (If children do not have spinners, make spinners using outstretched paper clips and pencils.) Read the directions for the game and then demonstrate it with children following along. Pretend that you are both players. When there is a trade to be made, have a child come to the projector to help you. The object of the game is to be the first player to get rid of all the blocks.

Practice
Have children decide whether they want to play in pairs, trios, or groups of four. Suggest that they put all of their base ten blocks in a central area for all to use during the game. Each child should have page 72. Observe children as they play the game.

Wrap-Up
Ask children what they did when there weren't enough ones to take away for a spin. Make sure all children can hear one another and share their experiences about the regrouping procedure.

Extension Activity
Play the Wipe Out Game using play money dimes and pennies or $10 and $1 bills.

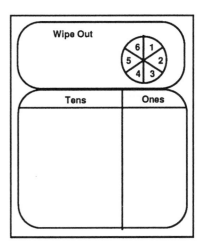

Trade Down

Wipe Out

Players: 2 or more

Materials: 5 tens blocks, 20 ones blocks per player, transparent spinner or paper clip and pencil

How to play: Each player starts with 5 tens on the mat. Take turns spinning the spinner and removing the appropriate number of ones. On the first turn each player must trade a ten for 10 ones before any ones can be removed. Trade and remove blocks until no blocks are left. When a player had 9 or fewer ones left, spin until the exact number of ones makes 0 or lose a turn.

How to win: Be the first player to get rid of all the blocks!

Ones Spinner

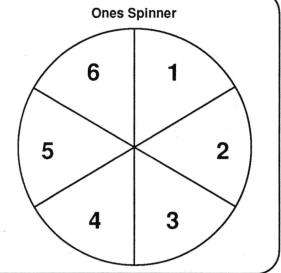

TENS	ONES

Base Ten Blocks

Overhead Manipulatives in Action, K–3
© 1992 Learning Resources, Inc.

Understanding Addition

✓ Objective

To solve an addition problem involving two-digit numbers using base ten blocks.

Vocabulary
tens, ones, add, sum, in all, altogether, total

Materials
Overhead Base Ten Blocks, transparencies of pages 63 and 74, overhead pens; *Base Ten Blocks*, student copies of pages 63 and 74, pencils

Warm-Up
Review the basic facts for addition. Make sure that children can recall the sums quickly. Also review how to regroup (trade) with two-digit numbers.

Activity
Distribute base ten blocks and page 63. Direct children to model your actions during this activity. Show 4 tens and 3 ones at the top of the page and ask what number is being represented. [43] Then show 2 tens and 6 ones in the lower portion of the page and ask what number is being represented. [26] Ask children how many blocks there are altogether. [69] Do more addition problems, including those involving regrouping, such as 27 + 38 or 32 + 48.

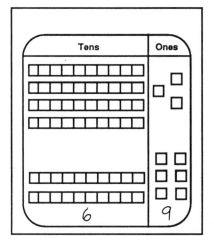

Practice
Distribute base ten blocks and page 74. Demonstrate the first problem. Place 2 tens and 3 ones and then 5 tens and 8 ones on the mat at the bottom of the page. Draw a picture of the blocks next to the problem, using lines and dots. Then combine the blocks, showing the regrouping of 11 ones to 1 ten and 1 one to get a total of 8 tens and 1 one, or 81. Ask questions during the demonstration. Have children finish the other three problems.

Wrap-Up
Ask volunteers to demonstrate how each sum was obtained.
Answers: 1. 81; 2. 75; 3. 57; 4. 70.

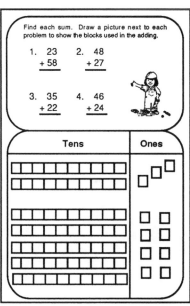

Extension Activity
Using base ten blocks and copies of page 63, have children find sums of three or four one- and two-digit numbers. They may wish to generate the addends by randomly selecting number squares 1–100 from a bag.

Addition

Find each sum. Draw a picture next to each problem to show the blocks used in the adding.

1. 23 ═══ ∴
    + 58 ═══ ∴
         ═══ ∴

2. 48
    + 27

3. 35
    + 22

4. 46
    + 24

TENS	ONES

Overhead Manipulatives in Action, K–3
© 1992 Learning Resources, Inc.

Understanding Subtraction

Objective

To solve a subtraction problem with two-digit numbers using base ten blocks.

Vocabulary
tens, ones, subtract, difference, how many left?

Materials
Overhead Base Ten Blocks, transparencies of pages 63 and 76, overhead pens; *Base Ten Blocks*, student copies of pages 63 and 76, pencils

Warm-Up
Review the basic facts for subtraction. Make sure that children can recall the differences quickly. Also review how to regroup (trade) with two-digit numbers.

Activity
Distribute base ten blocks and page 63. Direct children to model your actions during this activity. Show 3 tens and 8 ones at the top of the page and ask what number is being represented. [38] Then tell children that 24 will be taken away and ask how many blocks will be left. [14] Pause to allow children to figure out the answer. Then ask children for the answer and how they obtained it. Do more subtraction problems including those involving regrouping, such as 50 – 27 or 62 – 48. Select children to demonstrate the regrouping procedure at the projector for the class to see.

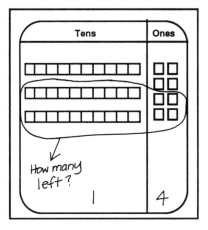

Practice
Distribute base ten blocks and page 76. Demonstrate the first problem. Place 4 tens and 6 ones on the mat at the bottom of the page. Draw a picture of the blocks next to the problem, using lines and dots. Then remove 14 blocks. Ask how many blocks are left. Direct children to finish the other three problems. Tell them to look at each problem to see if any of them needs regrouping before subtracting.

Wrap-Up
Ask volunteers to demonstrate how each subtraction problem was solved. Answers: 1. 32; 2. 14; 3. 20; 4. 33.

Extension Activity
Using play coins, have children buy various items and then obtain change from a quarter, half-dollar, or a multiple of ten cents.

Subtraction

Subtract. Draw a picture next to each problem to show the blocks used in the subtracting.

1. 46
   − 14
   ———

2. 50
   − 36
   ———

3. 83
   − 63
   ———

4. 61
   − 28
   ———

TENS	ONES

Overhead Manipulatives in Action, K–3
© 1992 Learning Resources, Inc.

Clocks

Introduction

The movable hands on the *Clock Dials* are especially helpful for demonstrating telling time to the hour, half hour, quarter hour, and minute and showing clockwise and counterclockwise directions to figure out elapsed time. By turning the hands forward or back, children can count forward or count back to mentally find solutions to "addition" and "subtraction" situations involving units of time.

Clock Activities

Getting Organized

Materials you will need:
- ◆ *Overhead Clock Dials* (LER 570)
- ◆ One transparency each of pages 80, 82, 84, 86, 88, 90
- ◆ Blank transparencies, overhead pens

Materials your students will need:
- ◆ *Pupil Clocks* (LER 112)
- ◆ Copies of pages 78, 80, 82, 84, 86, 88, 90
- ◆ Scissors, brass fasteners (brads), hole punch

The clock faces shown on page 78 are exact replicas of the *Overhead Clock Dial* except that one has a digital clockface attached to it. You and your students may use either type of clock dial. To attach the hour and minute hands to the clock dials, use a hole punch to make an opening for the brass fastener that will hold them in place, yet provide mobility of the hour and minute hands.

Getting Started

Initiate a discussion about instruments for telling time. Ask children whether they or their parents have a watch, or if they have an alarm clock or a digital clock radio. Ask about the different types of clocks they have seen—grandfather clocks, cuckoo clocks, mantel clocks. Point out that there are two different kinds of clocks, those with clock faces (analog) showing hour and minute hands that go around all the numbers and those showing only numbers (digital).

Ask children whether they pay attention to the time. Ask when they have to do a particular chore or when they watch their favorite television program. Have them talk about their day. Focus on terms *morning, afternoon,* and *evening.* Also concentrate on whether it is light or dark outdoors for a particular activity.

Clocks Dials

Clocks

Overhead Manipulatives in Action, K–3
© 1992 Learning Resources, Inc.

Hour Time

✓ Objective

To tell time to the hour.

Vocabulary

o'clock, numbers 1–12, hour time

Materials

Overhead Clock Dials, transparency of page 80, blank transparencies, overhead pens; *Pupil Clocks*, student copies of page 80, pencils

Warm-Up

Distribute pupil clocks. Display an overhead clock dial on the projector. Ask questions about the clock: **Do you see any numbers?** [yes] **Say the numbers.** [1, 2, 3, ... 12] **Did you find anything that moves?** [yes] **These are hands. The short hand is the hour hand and the long hand is the minute hand.** Direct children to follow along on their clocks during the presentation. **To tell time on the hour, say, 2:00, put the hour hand on the 2 and the minute hand on the 12. How would you show 7:00?** Go through all the hour times, either showing a time on the clock dial and asking for the time or saying an hour time and asking children to show the time on their clocks.

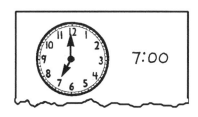

Activity

Show 8:00 on the clock dial. Tell children that this is a morning time. Ask what they are usually doing at this time in the morning. Tell them that 8:00 can also be an evening time and ask what they are usually doing at this time in the evening. Present several other hour times and discuss the times in relation to children's activities.

Practice

Hour Time. Cut the transparency of page 80 into four sections, one section per problem. Display the overhead clock dial and the "wake up" picture. Ask various children when they wake up in the morning. Ask them to find the hour time on their clocks and show the times to you. Record one of the times. You may wish to go through more of the problems on page 80 orally or distribute page 80 and then have children complete all of the problems.

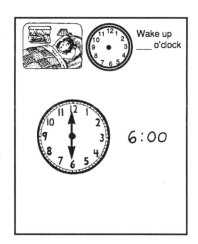

Wrap-Up

Discuss all the different hour times that children gave for the four problems on page 80.

Extension Activity

When discussing the hour times students gave for the problems, ask if the time was in the *morning, afternoon,* or *evening*. Perhaps the hour time was at *noon* or at *midnight*. Ask children how they could tell the difference in time if it were 8:00 in the morning or 8:00 in the evening. This is a springboard to presenting a lesson about A.M. and P.M. as well as *24-hour* time telling.

Hour Time

Activity	Draw hour time.	Write hour time.
		Wake up _____ o'clock
		Lunch _____ o'clock
		Math class _____ o'clock
		Dinner _____ o'clock

Overhead Manipulatives in Action, K–3
© 1992 Learning Resources, Inc.

Half-Hour Time

 **Objective**

To tell time on the half hour.

Vocabulary

o'clock, numbers 1–30, half past, half hour, clockwise

Materials

Overhead Clock Dials, transparency of page 82, blank transparencies, overhead pens; *Pupil Clocks*, student copies of page 82, pencils

Warm-Up

Have children count aloud from 1 to 30.

Activity

Distribute pupil clocks. Display the overhead clock dial on the projector. Set the hands at 10:00 and tell students to do the same. Ask how the hands would be moved around the clock to show half past 10:00. After some discussion, show how the hands move in a *clockwise* direction around the clock; the minute hand moves halfway around the clock and stops at 6, the hour hand is now halfway between 10 and 11. This is half past 10:00. Have children find half hour times as you either call out the time and they show it on their clocks, or as you show a half hour time on the overhead clock dial and they tell it. Tell the students that half past ten is many times called "ten thirty." Ask them how half past ten and "ten thirty" could be the same thing. Some children may notice the minute marks along the outer edge of the clock faces. There are 30 minute marks halfway around the clock. Have the children tell time using the "... thirty" phrase.

Practice

Half-Hour Time. Cut the transparency of page 82 into four sections, one section per problem. Display the overhead clock dial and the "breakfast" picture to the students. Ask volunteers when they eat breakfast in the morning. Ask them to find a half hour time on their clocks and show the times to you. Record one of the times. You may wish to go through more of the problems on page 82 orally or distribute the page and then have the children complete the problems.

Wrap-Up

Discuss all the different half hour times that the students gave for the four problems.

Extension Activity

Direct children to be more specific about telling time to the half hour by saying whether it is A.M. or P.M. time.

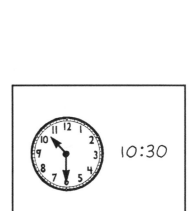

Half-Hour Time

Activity	Draw hour time.	Write hour time.
		**Breakfast** _____ o'clock
		**Lunch** _____ o'clock
		**Come home** _____ o'clock
		**Bedtime** _____ o'clock

Clocks

(82)

Overhead Manipulatives in Action, K–3
© 1992 Learning Resources, Inc.

Quarter-Hour Time

Objective

To tell time on the quarter hour.

Vocabulary

o'clock, quarter past, quarter to, fifteen, forty-five

Materials

Overhead Clock Dials, transparency of page 84, blank transparencies, overhead pens; *Pupil Clocks*, student copies of page 84, pencils

Warm-Up

Distribute pupil clocks. Place an overhead clock dial on the projector with a blank transparency over it. Ask children how they would divide the clock into four parts (fourths or quarters). Draw the lines on the transparency over the clock dial. Notice that the lines fall on the 12, 3, 6, and 9.

Note: Since this activity includes both *quarter after* and *quarter to* the hour, you may wish to split the presentation into two class sessions depending on ability.

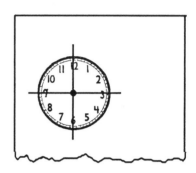

Activity

Quarter-Hour Time. Distribute page 84. Cut the transparency of page 84 in half and display the top half on the projector. Place the overhead clock dial over the picture of the clock face. Show 10:00 and then move the minute hand a quarter of the way around the clock clockwise to show 10:15 or *quarter past* 10. Ask where the hour hand should be at that time. [quarter of the way past 10] Move another quarter of the way around the clock and it's half past 10 or 10:30. Ask where the hour hand is now. [halfway between 10 and 11] Move another quarter of the way around the clock and it's three-quarters of an hour past 10 or a quarter hour to 11. Again, ask where the hour hand is. [closer to 11] After some manipulation with the clock dials and telling time, ask children why quarter past 10 is the same as 10:15. Notice the minute marks around the outer edge of the clock face. Count them by fives around the clock.

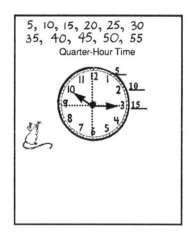

Practice

Assign the bottom portion of page 84 as class work. Permit children to use their clocks to help them draw the hands on the clock face pictures.

Wrap-Up

Discuss the problems on page 84. Ask volunteers to come to the projector to show the quarter-hour times designated by the problems.

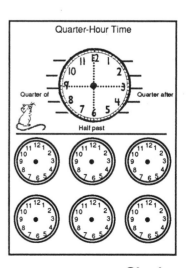

Quarter-Hour Time

Count by fives around the clock.

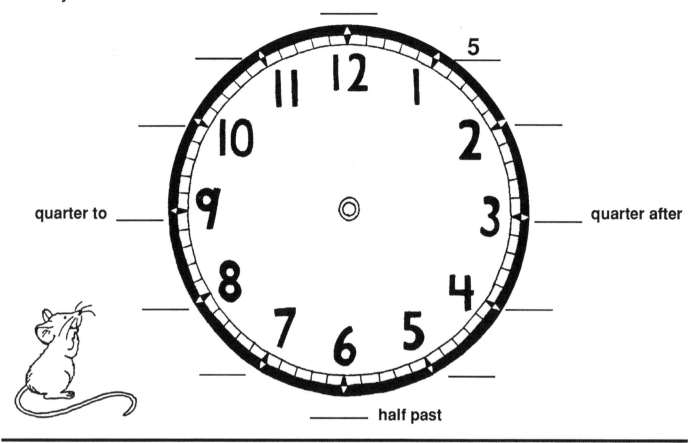

quarter to _____

quarter after _____

half past _____

Show these times on your clock. Then draw the hands for each time.

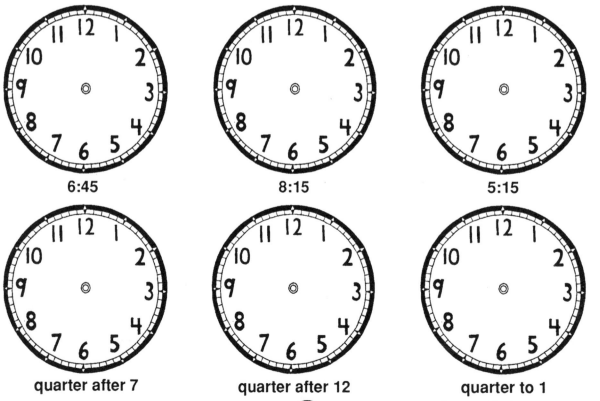

6:45

8:15

5:15

quarter after 7

quarter after 12

quarter to 1

Clocks

(84)

Overhead Manipulatives in Action, K–3
© 1992 Learning Resources, Inc.

Minute Time

Objective

To tell time to the minute.

Vocabulary

o'clock, numbers 1–60, minute(s), after, to

Materials

Overhead Clock Dials, transparency of page 86, blank transparencies, overhead pens; *Pupil Clocks*, student copies of page 86, pencils

Warm-Up

Direct children in counting activities from 1 to 60 by fives and by tens. Ask them how long they think a minute is. Have them count slowly from 1 to 60 while you keep time on your watch for one minute.

Activity

Minute Time. Distribute page 86 and pupil clocks. Cut the transparency of page 86 in half and display the top half on the projector. Place an overhead clock dial over the picture of the clock face. Direct children to follow along and count aloud by ones from 1 to 59 as you move the minute hand around the clock dial in a clockwise direction. Ask children how they would count by fives around the clock face. Note that the five-minute intervals fall on the numerals 1 to 12 around the clock face.

Practice

Five-Minute Times. Show the time 8:05 on the overhead clock dial and tell children it is "five minutes after eight." Do several five-minute times for 5, 10, 15, 20, 25, and 30 minutes after the hour. Then show five-minute times for 35, 40, 45, 50, and 55 minutes after the hour. Since these times are getting closer to the next hour, there are two ways to say these times. For example, 8:50 can be said as "eight fifty" or "ten to nine." Ask children why the time can be said both ways. Have them find five-minute times either by calling out the time and then showing the time on their clocks or by showing a five-minute time on the overhead clock dial and having children tell the time.

One-Minute Times. Repeat the procedure for one-minute times. Then assign the bottom portion of page 86 as class work.

Wrap-Up

Discuss the problems on page 86. Ask volunteers to come to the projector to show the minute times designated by the problems. Ask children why there isn't a time like 4:60.

Minute Times

Count by ones around the clock.

Show these times on your clock. Then draw the hands for each time.

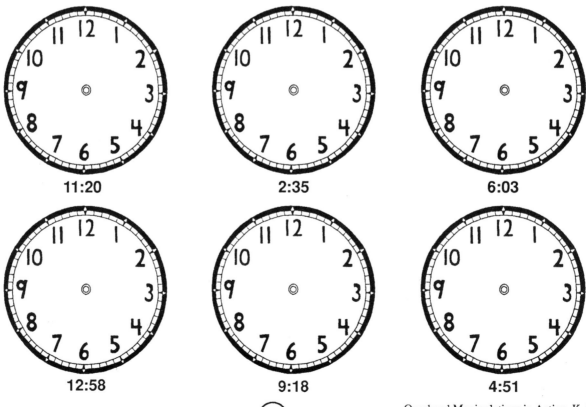

| 11:20 | 2:35 | 6:03 |
| 12:58 | 9:18 | 4:51 |

Clocks

(86)

Time from Now

 **Objective**

To figure out elapsed time from now. (Adding with units of time.)

Vocabulary

time from now, clockwise

Materials

Overhead Clock Dials, transparency of page 88, blank transparencies, overhead pens; *Pupil Clocks*, student copies of page 88, pencils

Warm-Up

Have children count on by ones and then by fives from designated numbers.

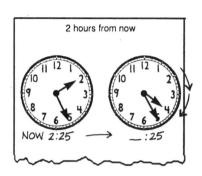

2 hours from now

NOW 2:25 ⟶ __:25

Activity

Time from Now—Hours. Display two overhead clock dials on the projector. Set the time 2:00 on both clocks. Ask children what time it will be four hours from now. Also ask how they would figure out the answer. After some discussion, move the hour hand clockwise four hours from 2 to 6 on the second clock to show children that four hours have elapsed. Ask children what happens to the minute hand on a real clock when four hours pass. Examples:

3:15, 5 hours from now [8:15] **5:30, 8 hours from now** [1:30]
2:25, 2 hours from now [4:25] **9:17, 12 hours from now** [9:17]

Time from Now—Minutes. Use the same procedure, this time moving the minute hand around the clock face in a clockwise direction to find the time from now. Try these examples:

1:30, 20 minutes from now [1:50] **4:40, 30 minutes from now** [5:10]

Time from Now—Hours and Minutes. This time children must use both the hour and minute hands to figure out the elapsed time from now. Examples:

8:00, 2 hours and 15 minutes from now [10:15]
2:45, 1 hour and 35 minutes from now [4:20]

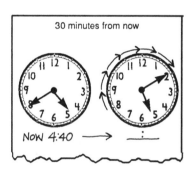

30 minutes from now

NOW 4:40 ⟶ __:__

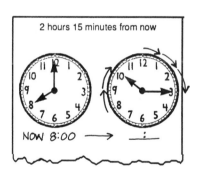

2 hours 15 minutes from now

NOW 8:00 ⟶ __:__

Practice

Children may work in pairs to complete page 88. Have them draw a picture or write a short story in each box for a "time from now" scenario and then show the time *now* and the *time from now*.

Wrap-Up

Have children discuss their time stories with each other.

Extension Activity

Show children how to calculate the elapsed time from now. Examples:

6:30, 2 hours from now	5:40, 35 minutes from now	11:26, 2 hours and 14 minutes from now
6:30	5:40	11:26
+ 2:00	+ 0:35	+ 2:14
8:30	--4:75-	--13:40-
	5:15	1:40

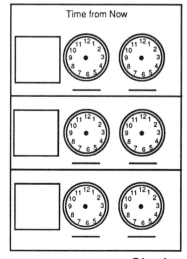

Time from Now

Time from Now

Activity	NOW	TIME FROM NOW

Draw a picture or write a short story.

→

_____   _____

→

_____   _____

→

_____   _____

Clocks

(88)

Overhead Manipulatives in Action, K–3
© 1992 Learning Resources, Inc.

Time Ago

Objective

To figure out elapsed time ago. (Subtracting with units of time.)

Vocabulary
time ago, counterclockwise

Materials
Overhead Clock Dials, transparency of page 90, blank transparencies, overhead pens; *Pupil Clocks*, student copies of page 90, pencils

Warm-Up
Have children count back by ones and then by fives from designated numbers.

Activity
Time Ago—Hours. Display two overhead clock dials on the projector. Set the time 2:00 on both clocks. Ask children what time it was four hours ago. Also ask them how they figured out the answer. After some discussion, move the hour hand *counterclockwise* four hours from 2 to 10 on the second clock to show time four hours ago. Do more examples, such as these:

8:15, 5 hours ago [3:15]   **5:30, 1 hour ago** [4:30]
2:25, 2 hours ago [12:25]   **9:33, 12 hours ago** [9:33]

Time Ago—Minutes. Use the same procedure, this time moving the minute hand around the clock face in a counterclockwise direction to find the time ago. Try these examples:

9:30, 15 minutes ago [9:15]   **4:16, 30 minutes ago** [3:46]

Time Ago—Hours and Minutes. This time children must use both the hour and minute hands to figure out the elapsed time. Examples:

8:40, 2 hours and 15 minutes ago [6:25]
5:10, 4 hours and 20 minutes ago [12:50]

Practice
Children may work in pairs to complete the three problems on page 90. They can draw a picture or write a short story in each box for a "time from now" scenario and then show the time *now* and the *time ago*.

Wrap-Up
Have children discuss their time stories with each other.

Extension Activity
Show children how to calculate the elapsed time ago. Here are three examples:

6:30, 2 hours ago	5:10, 35 minutes ago	11:26, 2 hours and 40 minutes ago
	4:70	11:86
6:30	~~5:10~~	~~11:26~~
− 2:00	− 0:35	− 2:40
4:30	4:35	9:46

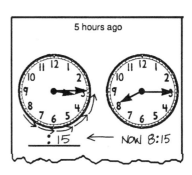
5 hours ago

:15 ← NOW 8:15

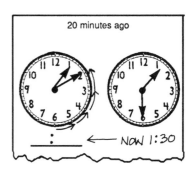
20 minutes ago

: ← NOW 1:30

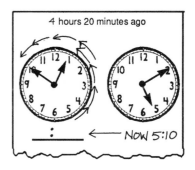
4 hours 20 minutes ago

: ← NOW 5:10

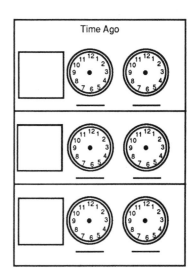
Time Ago

Time Ago

	TIME AGO	NOW

Draw a picture or write a short story.

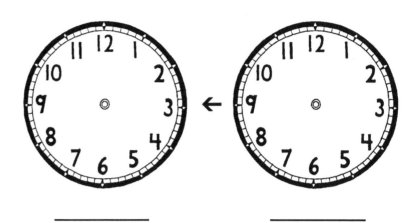

_____   _____

_____   _____

_____   _____

Clocks

(90)

Overhead Manipulatives in Action, K–3
© 1992 Learning Resources, Inc.

Coins

Introduction

Using the *Coin Set* not only gives children the opportunity to learn about money, but it also reinforces major number concepts. By manipulating the play money in the *Coin Set*, children can learn the value of each coin, find coin equivalences, count and combine amounts of money, and make change. And, since the coins in this set are realistic replicas of actual coins, children should be able to make a natural transition to handling real coins in their daily lives. The use of money lends itself especially well to developing mental math skills dealing with equivalences, addition (combining amounts of money), and subtraction (making change).

Coin Activities

Pages   93–94   Penny, Nickel, Dime
          95–96   Quarter
          97–98   Half-Dollar
          99–100   Counting Money
          101–102   Going Shopping
          103–104   Making Change

Getting Organized

Materials you will need:
- ◆ *Overhead Coin Set* (LER 625)
- ◆ Real coins
- ◆ One transparency each of pages 94, 96, 98, 100, 102, 104
- ◆ Blank transparencies, overhead pens, sheet of paper

Materials your students will need:
- ◆ *Coin Set* (LER 101, LER 95–99)
- ◆ Copies of pages 92, 94, 96, 98, 100, 102, 104
- ◆ Crayons or color markers, scissors, pencils, paper
- ◆ Optional: *Coin Stamps—Heads* (LER 102), *Coin Stamps—Tails* (LER 103)

Have children color the pennies brown before cutting out the coins on page 92.

Getting Started

Distribute small amounts of play money. Depending on grade level and/or ability, you may wish to use only one type of coin (pennies) in kindergarten, two to three types of coins (pennies, nickels, and dimes) in first grade, or perhaps all the coins at the same time. Ask children what they know about the coins. Some may be able to identify the coins and give the value. Some may talk about the features—person or symbol—on each head and tail.

Initiate a discussion regarding the use of money in daily life. How is it used? Do children have any money? Do they go shopping?

You may wish to show children some real coins and discuss how they are similar to and different from the play coins. At this time, you can point out some unique features, such as the penny is a different color from the other coins and the dime has ridges.

Coins

Overhead Manipulatives in Action, K–3
© 1992 Learning Resources, Inc.

Penny, Nickel, Dime

✓ Objective

To identify pennies, nickels, and dimes and their values.

Vocabulary

penny, nickel, dime, cent(s)

Materials

Overhead Coins, transparency of page 94, overhead pens, sheet of paper; *Coin Set*, student copies of page 94, pencils

Warm-Up

Direct children in a counting activity for the numbers 1–10. Depending on children's ability or the goal of this lesson, you many wish to have children review the basic facts for the sums of 5 and 10.

Activity

Identify Penny, Nickel, Dime. Distribute sets of coins. Using the overhead coins, show a penny (head) on the projector. Ask children to find the coin and to identify it if they can. Then show the tail of a penny and ask children to find and identify it. Talk about the features of the penny—color, person, symbols, words. Use the same procedure to familiarize children with the nickel and the dime.

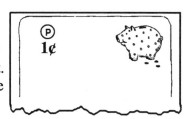

Practice

Value of Penny, Nickel, Dime; Coin Equivalents. Distribute sets of coins and page 94. Place the transparency of page 94 on the projector. Cover the nickel and dime sections of the page so that the class can focus on the penny. Place a penny (head) over the picture of the penny on the page and ask children to do the same. Tell them that a penny is worth one cent. Write 1¢.

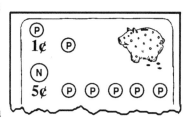

Move the paper down on the transparency to focus on the nickel. Place a nickel on the picture of the nickel and tell children that it is worth much more than a penny—five cents! Then write 5¢. Ask children to think about this: **If a nickel is worth five cents, how many pennies would that be?** After a brief discussion, display five pennies next to the nickel.

Remove the paper from the bottom part of the transparency to focus on the dime. Tell children that the dime is worth more than the penny—ten cents. Ask them to think about these coin equivalents: **If a dime is worth ten cents, how many pennies would that be? How many nickels would that be? Can you show other ways to show how much a dime is worth using pennies and nickels?** After each question, show the coin equivalents in pennies, nickels, and a combination of both.

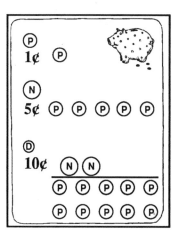

Wrap-Up

Play Coin Value Flash. Show a penny, nickel, or dime on the projector for a few seconds and then ask children to respond. Do several exercises in quick succession.

Penny, Nickle, Dime

Overhead Manipulatives in Action, K–3
© 1992 Learning Resources, Inc.

Quarter

 **Objective**

To identify a quarter and its value.

Vocabulary

quarter, penny, nickel, dime, cents

Materials

Overhead Coins, transparency of page 96, overhead pens; *Coin Set*, student copies of page 96, pencils, coin cutouts (page 92), paste, paper

Warm-Up

Direct children in a counting activity for the numbers 1–25 by ones and then by fives.

Activity

Identify the Quarter. Distribute sets of coins. Using the overhead coins, place a quarter (head) on the projector. Ask children to find the coin and to identify it if they can. Then show the tail of a quarter and ask children to find and identify it. Talk about the features of the quarter—color, person, symbols, words—and how its size compares with the penny, nickel, and dime. Ask: **Since the quarter is larger, do you think it is worth more than the other coins?** You may wish to follow up with a dime and penny to show them that size does not always count when it comes to coins.

Practice

Value of the Quarter; Coin Equivalents. Distribute sets of coins and page 96. Place a quarter on the picture of the quarter on the page and ask children to do the same. Tell them that the quarter is worth 25 cents and write 25¢. Ask children to think about these relationships: **If a quarter is worth 25 cents, how many pennies would that be? How many nickels? How many dimes? How many dimes and nickels?** After each question, show the coin equivalents in pennies, nickels, and dimes and nickels. When children find the value in nickels, place five nickels on the transparency and have them count by fives with you. Ask children if they can show other ways to make 25 cents using pennies, nickels, and dimes. Direct them either to make a list of all the possibilities or to paste cutouts of the coins on page 96 or paper.

Wrap-Up

Discuss the results of the practice activity. There are 13 ways to show 25 cents.

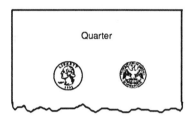

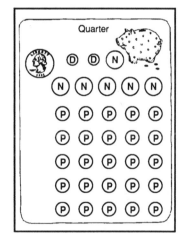

Solutions:

1 quarter
2 dimes, 1 nickel
2 dimes, 5 pennies
1 dime, 3 nickels
1 dime, 2 nickels, 5 pennies
1 dime, 1 nickel, 10 pennies
1 dime, 15 pennies
5 nickels
4 nickels, 5 pennies
3 nickels, 10 pennies
2 nickels, 15 pennies
1 nickel, 20 pennies
25 pennies

Quarter

Overhead Manipulatives in Action, K–3
© 1992 Learning Resources, Inc.

Half-Dollar

✓ Objective
To identify a half-dollar and its value.

Vocabulary
half-dollar, quarter, penny, nickel, dime, cents

Materials
Overhead Coins, transparency of page 98, overhead pens; *Coin Set*, student copies of page 98, pencils, coin cutouts (page 92), paste, paper

Warm-Up
Direct children in a counting activity for the numbers 1–50 by ones and then by fives and tens.

Activity
Identify the Half-Dollar. Distribute sets of coins. Using the overhead coins, place a half-dollar (head) on the projector. Ask children to find the coin and to identify it if they can. Then show the tail of a half-dollar and ask children to find and identify it. Talk about the features of the half-dollar—color, person, symbols, words—and how its size compares with the penny, nickel, dime, and quarter. Ask: **Since the half-dollar is larger, do you think it is worth more than the other coins?** You may then wish to remind them that this is not always the case, as with the penny and dime.

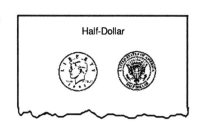

Half-Dollar

Practice
Value of the Half-Dollar; Coin Equivalents. Distribute sets of coins and page 98. Place a half-dollar on the picture of the half-dollar and ask children to do the same. Tell them that the half-dollar is worth 50 cents and write 50¢. Ask children to think about these relationships: **If a half-dollar is worth 50 cents, how many pennies would that be? How many nickels? How many dimes? How many quarters? How many dimes and nickels?** After each question, show the coin equivalents in pennies, nickels, dimes, and quarters. When children find the value in nickels, place ten nickels on the transparency and have them count by fives with you. When students find the value in dimes, place five dimes on the transparency and have them count by tens with you. Ask if they can show other ways to make 50 cents using pennies, nickels, dimes, and quarters. Direct them either to make a list of all the possibilities or to paste cutouts of the coins on page 92 on paper. (If you have rubber coin stamps and an ink pad, have children record the possibilities in an organized list.) Assign as a class project, since there are 50 possible ways to show 50 cents.

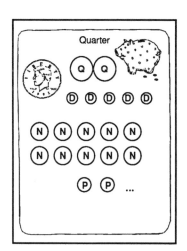

Quarter

Wrap-Up
Discuss the results of the practice activity above.

Half-Dollar

Overhead Manipulatives in Action, K–3
© 1992 Learning Resources, Inc.

Counting Money

Objectives

To count amounts of money.
To order coins by their value.

Vocabulary

count, amount

Materials

Overhead Coins, transparency of page 100, blank transparencies, overhead pens; *Coin Set*, student copies of page 100, pencils

Warm-Up

Direct children in some *counting on* exercises. For example, start with 6 and then count on to 10 by ones. Or start with 15 and count on by fives.

Activity

Distribute sets of coins and page 100. Depending on children's ability, you may wish to do the following tasks in one day or over several days.

Counting Same-Type Coins. Show six pennies in the coin purse on page 100. Ask children to count the money and state the total. Then show how the coins can be put into a straight line to make the counting process easier. Write the amount in the box. Do the same for nickels and then dimes, putting them in a line and then counting by fives and tens respectively.

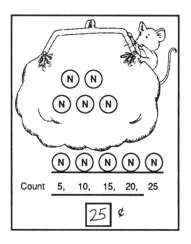

Count   5,   10,   15,   20,   25

25 ¢

Counting Different Types of Coins. Show two dimes and three pennies in the purse on page 100. Ask children how they would count the coins and tell the total. After some students respond, show how the counting process can be made easier by putting the coins in a line (two lines shown on page 100) in order of the coin's value—dime, dime, penny, penny, penny—and then count this way: 10, 20, 21, 22, 23. Write 23¢ in the box. Do several examples until children instinctively start to count the amount of money with the higher-value coins first.

Practice

Have children work in pairs. Using sets of coins and page 100, have one child put some coins in the purse and the partner count the money. Encourage children to count the higher-value coins first. Children should correct and help each other during the counting process. Observe as they count the coins.

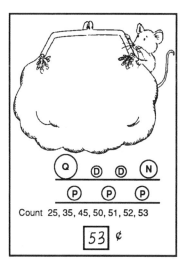

Count 25, 35, 45, 50, 51, 52, 53

53 ¢

Wrap-Up

Ask volunteers to help you count amounts of money. Using the transparency of page 100 and the overhead coins, place some coins in the purse and then ask a child to find the total amount for the coins.

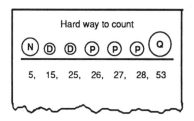

Hard way to count

5, 15, 25, 26, 27, 28, 53

Counting Money

¢

Overhead Manipulatives in Action, K–3
© 1992 Learning Resources, Inc.

Going Shopping

 Objectives

To match sets of coins with written amounts of money.
To find the total amount for two or more purchased items. (addition)

Vocabulary

total, amount

Materials

Overhead Coins, transparency of page 102, blank transparencies, overhead pens;
Coin Set, student copies of page 102, pencils

Warm-Up

Initiate a discussion about shopping. Bring some sale pages from the newspaper
to class. (Try to find advertisements involving cent amounts.) Since most or all
of the children have probably accompanied a family member to a store or
restaurant, ask them about how things are purchased and paid for.

Activity

Going Shopping. (Matching sets of coins to written amounts) Distribute sets of
coins and page 102. Select an item shown on page 102 and circle it. If you
choose the balloon, for example, ask children how much it costs and which coins
they need to pay for it. Although there are several possible ways to make 15
cents with coins, stress that it is easiest to use the fewest number of coins. Of
course, for 15 cents, a dime and a nickel or three nickels are both easy as
opposed to using all pennies or a combination of pennies and nickels. We use the
fewest number of coins to avoid counting mistakes. After the coins are shown at
the bottom of the page and counted aloud, write 15¢ in the box.

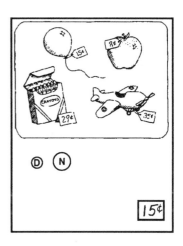

Find the Total Amount. Tell children that they are now going shopping and can
buy two items shown on page102. Direct them to follow along during the
examples. Select two items and circle them. Show and count the amount of
money for the first item and then the second item. Then ask: **How would you
find the total amount for both items?** (Pause to get some responses.) **Can we
put the two amounts of money together and then count all the money?** After
the two separate sets of coins have been combined and counted, write the total
amount in the box. Do another example.

Practice

Direct children to work in pairs to play Store—one child is the buyer, the other is
the storekeeper. Have them find the total amount of money for two, three, or all
four of the items shown on the page. Allow children to check their totals using
calculators or a toy cash register.

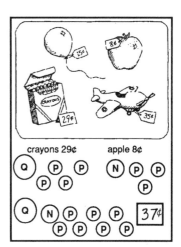

Wrap-Up

Discuss the activity. You may have children write an addition problem for the
items purchased. The problem can be written above the box on page 102.

Going Shopping

Overhead Manipulatives in Action, K–3
© 1992 Learning Resources, Inc.

Making Change

 Objectives

To figure out the exact coins or nearly the exact coins needed for a purchase. (compare numbers)
To make change. (subtraction)

Vocabulary
make change

Materials
Overhead Coins, transparency of page 104, blank transparencies; *Coin Set*, student copies of page 104

Warm-Up
Review coin equivalents for a nickel, dime, quarter, and half-dollar, and combinations of coins.

Activity
Using Enough Coins. Distribute sets of coins and page 104. Display the transparency of page 104, select an item at the top of the page, and circle it—for example, the dinosaur toy for 28¢. Tell children that you do not have the exact coins to make 28¢, but that you have a quarter and some dimes and nickels in your purse. Ask children which coins you could use to buy the toy. Tell them to find the fewest number of coins that total more than 28¢. [30¢; quarter, nickel] Since 30 > 28, the toy can be purchased and some change should be given in return. Do several exercises like this to get students to estimate the number of coins needed to purchase an item when they do not have the exact amount. Wait until children have mastered the skill in this activity before making change.

Enough money?

Making Change. Distribute sets of coins and page 104. Display the transparency of page 104 on the projector and circle one of the items, say, the muffin for 13¢. Ask: **How much does the muffin cost?** [13¢] **If you do not have exactly 13¢, which coins can you use to buy the muffin?** [Accept any combinations of 15¢ or more.] **If I give the storekeeper a dime and a nickel for the muffin, how much change should I get back?** [2¢] Show how the storekeeper accepts the 15¢ and how the change is made, trading five pennies for the nickel and then giving back only two pennies as change. Show children how to give change to a customer by saying: **The muffin is 13¢. So 13¢** (point to the muffin), **14¢** (give a penny), **15¢** (give another penny). **Your change is 2¢. Thank you.** Get children into the habit of using the *counting on* technique to make change before writing a subtraction problem for the transaction.

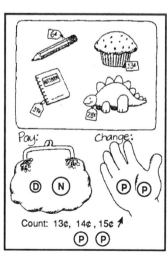

Practice
Have children work in pairs using sets of coins and page 104. Have one child be the customer and the other be the storekeeper.

Wrap-Up
Discuss the activity. Ask if anyone purchased more than one item and then was given the correct amount of change.

Making Change

Pay:

Change:

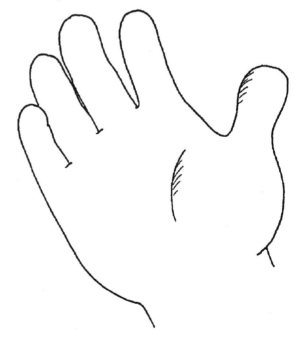

Coins

Fraction Circles

Introduction

Overhead Fraction Circles are useful for teaching unit fractions and proper fractions, finding equivalent fractions, comparing fractions, and investigating how fractional parts relate to each other and to whole numbers. By finding several ways to show the fractional number *one-half* or the whole number *one*, children gain valuable knowledge about combining fractional parts to make a larger quantity. When children are asked to add fractions with common or unlike denominators to equal 1/2, 3/4, or 1 in future grades, these primary grade experiences will have provided them with a solid foundation.

Fraction Circle Activities

 ## Getting Organized

Materials you will need:
   ◆ *Overhead Fraction Circles* (LER 315)
   ◆ One transparency each of pages 106, 110, 112, 114, 116, 118, 120
   ◆ Blank transparencies, overhead pens, sheet of paper, two apples, orange, knife, business envelope

Materials students will need:
   ◆ *Circular Fraction Set* (LER 115)
   ◆ Copies of pages 106, 107, 108, 110, 112, 114, 116, 118, 120
   ◆ Crayons or color markers, scissors, paste, pencils, paper

Note: Since page 106 is used in five lessons, duplicate at least five times the number of copies so that you will have enough for the lessons on pages 111–120.

 ## Getting Started

Before children are shown the *Circular Fraction Sets*, initiate a discussion about how a candy bar, a cake, or a pizza can be divided evenly between a pair or small group of children. You may wish to have children experiment with actual candy bars or a pizza to find solutions. Stress the fact that all of the parts must be of equal size for everyone to get a fair share. Allow children to explore with their *Circular Fraction Sets* before you begin formal activities. Observe and listen carefully to children's comments about the fraction pieces. Some students may discover that two orange pieces (halves) make a whole circle or that all the pieces in each color are equal in size. With very young children, you may wish to refer to the circles as small pies or cookies. Ask how they would share a "pie" or a "cookie" with two, three, four, six, or eight friends. Ask if the size of each part must be the same to get a fair share. Dividing a region into equal-sized pieces to show unit-fraction parts is a very important concept. It is also important for children to discover that a region divided into more equal-sized pieces has smaller sized pieces; for example, fourths are smaller than thirds for a region of the same size.

Fraction Circles

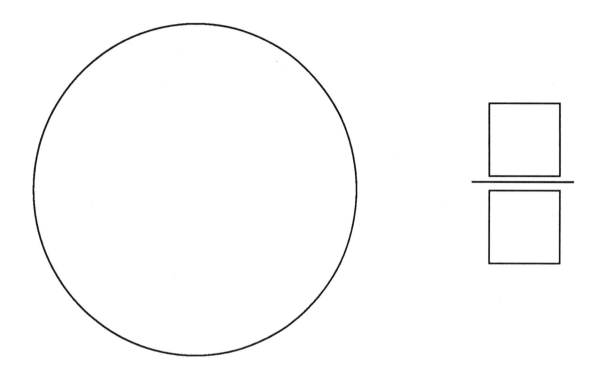

Overhead Manipulatives in Action, K–3
© 1992 Learning Resources, Inc.

Fraction Circles

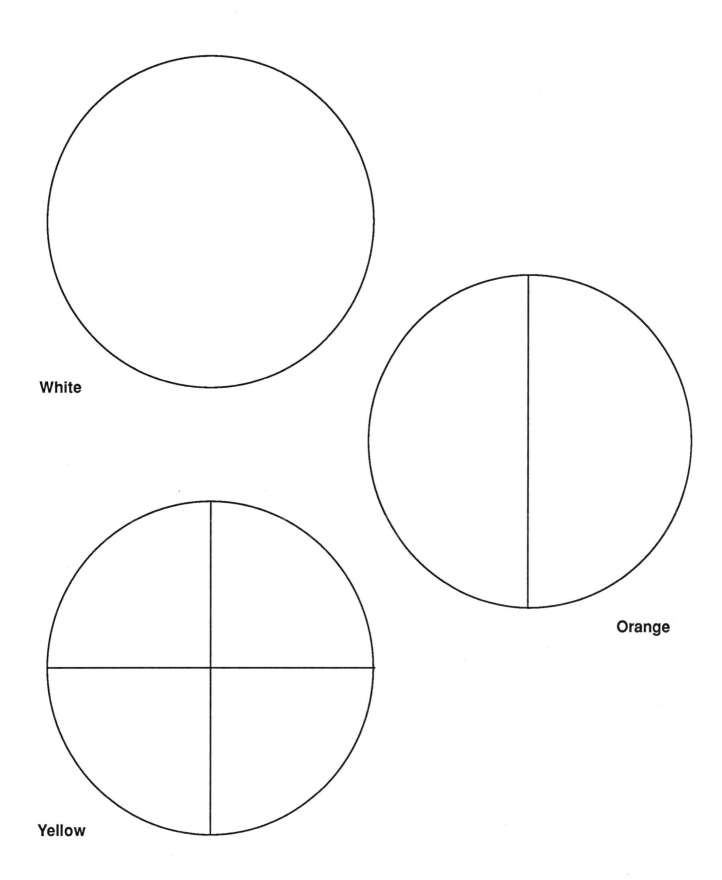

White

Orange

Yellow

Fraction Circles

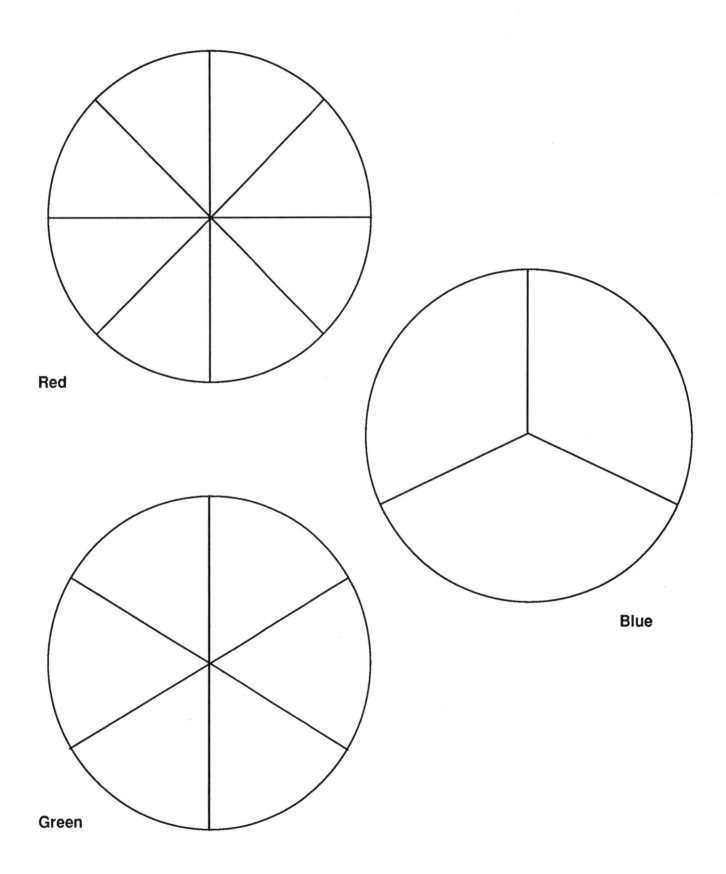

Red

Blue

Green

Overhead Manipulatives in Action, K–3
© 1992 Learning Resources, Inc.

One and Halves

 Objective

To recognize one whole and halves.

Vocabulary

one, fair share, one-half

Materials

Overhead Fraction Circles, transparency of page 110,
blank transparency, overhead pens, paper, two apples, knife; *Circular Fraction
Sets*, student copies of page 110, pencils, crayons

Warm-Up

Display a piece of fruit such as an apple. Cut it into two pieces so that one piece
is obviously larger than the other. Ask: **How many pieces are there now?** [2]
Select two children and ask one of them: **Which piece do you want? If both of
you wanted a "fair share" of this apple, how would you cut the apple?** Show
another apple and cut it in half as accurately as possible. Ask: **How many pieces
are there now?** [2] Select two children and ask one of them: **Which piece of the
apple would you like?** Children may be somewhat hesitant if the pieces are very
equal in size. Ask: **Would you get a fair share choosing either piece?** Repeat
the activity, this time cutting an orange into fourths or a pizza into eighths.
Children should come to realize that in order to split something into "fair
shares," the pieces must be of equal size.

Cut an apple   Cut a small
in half.   piece of apple.

Activity

Distribute sets of fraction circles and page 110. Display the transparency of page
110 on the projector, covering the bottom half of the page with a sheet of paper.
Focusing on the circle at the top, ask children to find one piece that fits the
circle. Discuss. Remove the paper to reveal the circle with two pieces. Ask
children whether they think the pieces (parts) are the same size. Since there are
two equal-sized pieces, then each piece is 1/2.

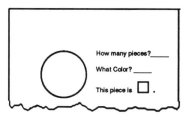

Practice

Direct children to fill in the answer blanks and boxes on page 110 and to color
one of the fraction pieces to show 1/2.

Wrap-Up

Ask children about which half of the bottom circle they colored. Ask them which
side they think is correct and why.

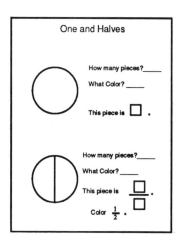

Fraction Circles

Ones and Halves

How many pieces? _____

What color? _____

This piece is [ ] .

How many pieces? _____

What color? _____

This piece is $\dfrac{\boxed{}}{\boxed{}}$.

Color $\dfrac{1}{2}$.

Overhead Manipulatives in Action, K–3
© 1992 Learning Resources, Inc.

Fourths and Eighths

 Objective

To recognize fourths and eighths.

Vocabulary

fraction, one-fourth, one-eighth, numerator, denominator

Materials

Overhead Fraction Circles, transparencies of pages 106 and 112, blank transparency, overhead pens; *Circular Fraction Sets*, student copies of pages 106, 107, 108, and 112, pencils, crayons, scissors

Warm-Up

Distribute pages 107 and 108. Direct children to color and cut out the fraction circle pieces.

Activity

Distribute page 106. You may wish to distribute sets of circular fractions or have children use their own newly made sets. Display the transparency of page 106 on the projector. Proceed as follows: Place the orange pieces on the circle. **How many pieces?** [2] Remove one orange piece. **What part of the circle is orange?** [1 part] **So the circle shows that 1 of the 2 pieces is orange, or 1/2. Write 1 in the top box and write 2 in the bottom box to show the fraction *1/2*. The numbers in a fraction have names—the top number is the *numerator*, the bottom number is the *denominator*. The denominator tells how many parts the circle is divided into; the numerator tells how many parts we are talking about.** Show examples for fourths and eighths in the same manner. Focus on unit fractions 1/4 and 1/8 at this time.

Practice

Distribute page 112 and display the transparency of the page on the projector. Talk about the top circle of fractional parts (fourths). Ask: **If each piece is 1/4, how would you show 2/4? 3/4? 4/4?** Have children complete the page independently.

Wrap-Up

Display the transparency when you discuss the problems on page 112 . Although children found 1/8 and colored 5/8 for the bottom circle, ask how they would show 2/8, 3/8, 4/8, 6/8, 7/8 and 8/8. Could they show 9/8? Ask them if they noticed anything special about the amount of space that was covered for 1/4 and 2/8, or 2/4 and 4/8, or 3/4 and 6/8.

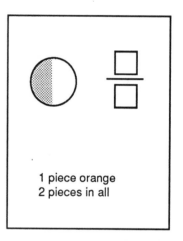

1 piece orange
2 pieces in all

Easy way to remember where the numerator and denominator are in a fraction:

numerator → ☐ up
denominator → ☐ down

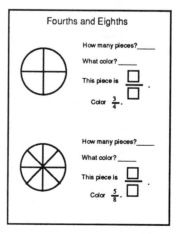

Fraction Circles

Fourths and Eighths

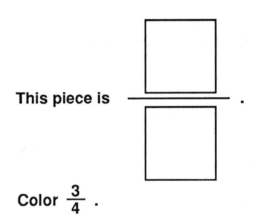

How many pieces? _____

What color? _____

This piece is $\dfrac{\quad}{\quad}$.

Color $\dfrac{3}{4}$.

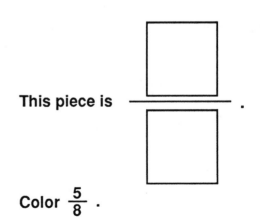

How many pieces? _____

What color? _____

This piece is $\dfrac{\quad}{\quad}$.

Color $\dfrac{5}{8}$.

Fraction Circles

(112)

Overhead Manipulatives in Action, K–3
© 1992 Learning Resources, Inc.

Thirds and Sixths

 Objective

To recognize thirds and sixths.

Vocabulary

fraction, one-third, one-sixth, numerator, denominator

Materials

Overhead Fraction Circles, transparencies of pages 106 and 114, a blank transparency, overhead pens, sheet of paper, business envelope; *Circular Fraction Sets*, student copies of pages 106 and 114, pencils, crayons, paper

Warm-Up

Ask children to take out a sheet of notebook paper and write a short letter (a sentence or two) to a friend telling what they have learned about fractions. Then ask them to fold the letter into thirds so that it could be mailed in an envelope (show them the envelope). Observe whether children estimate the thirds by rolling the paper into thirds before actually pressing the folds into the paper. Go around to each child to see if the folded letter fits into your envelope. Next challenge children to make one more fold in the letter to show sixths (there are two ways).

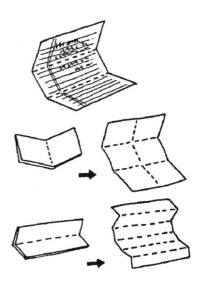

Activity

Distribute page 106 and sets of circular fractions. Display the transparency of page 106 on the projector. Proceed as follows: Place the blue pieces on the circle. **How many pieces?** [3] **Remove all but one blue piece. What part of the circle is blue?** [1 part] **So the circle shows that 1 of the 3 pieces is blue, or 1/3. Write 1 in the top box, write 3 in the bottom box to show the fraction *1/3*. Which number is the *numerator*?** [1] **Which number is the *denominator*?** [3] **What does 1/3 mean?** Show examples for sixths. Focus on unit fractions 1/3 and 1/6 at this time.

Practice

Distribute page 114 and display the transparency of page 114 on the projector. Talk about the top circle of fractional parts (thirds). Ask: **If each piece is 1/3, how would you show 2/3? 3/3?** Have children complete the page independently.

Wrap-Up

Display the transparency of page 114 when you discuss the problems. Although children colored 2/3 and 5/6 for the problems, ask them how they would show 1/3, 3/3, 1/6, 2/6, 3/6, 4/6, and 6/6. Could they show 5/3 or 7/6? Ask if they noticed anything special about the amount of space that was covered for 1/3 and 2/6 or 2/3 and 4/6.

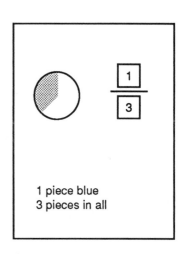

Fraction Circles

Thirds and Sixths

How many pieces? _____

What color? _____

This piece is ⬜/⬜ .

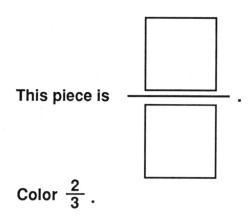

Color $\frac{2}{3}$.

How many pieces? _____

What color? _____

This piece is ⬜/⬜ .

Color $\frac{5}{6}$.

Overhead Manipulatives in Action, K–3
© 1992 Learning Resources, Inc.

Compare Fractions

 Objective

To compare fractional numbers using circular regions.

Vocabulary

compare, equivalent, greater than, less than

Materials

Overhead Fraction Circles, transparencies of pages 106 and 116, a blank transparency, overhead pens; *Circular Fraction Sets*, student copies of page 116, pencils

Warm-Up

Play the Fraction Flash Game. Display the transparency of page 106 on the projector. Tell children that you are going to show a fraction picture to them for only a few seconds and then shut off the projector. Ask them to respond quickly. After each fraction, ask children how they would write the fraction for the fraction picture. Try to cover as many halves, thirds, fourths, sixths, and eighths as possible in a few minutes.

Activity

Distribute page 116 and sets of circular fractions. Display the transparency of page 116 on the projector. Place one orange piece on the first circle and one yellow piece on the second circle. Ask children to do the same and then to name the fractional parts of each circle. [1/2, 1/4] Ask which fractional part is larger. Write the words *is larger than* or *is greater than* between the two fraction numerals, or use the symbols < or >. Try another example showing two fractional parts that are equivalent, such as 1/2 and 3/6 or 1/4 and 2/8. Write the word *equivalent* or place the symbol = between the fraction numerals.

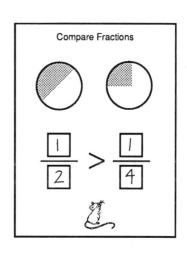

Practice

Have children work in cooperative groups of three or four to find pairs of fractional numbers equivalent to each other or one larger than the other. When all children complete the page, they can bind it into a book showing fractional number comparisons.

Wrap-Up

Have groups present their fraction pictures to the class. Some children may wish to show their fractional comparisons on the projector using overhead fraction circles.

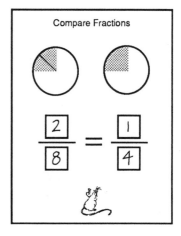

Fraction Circles

Compare Fractions

Overhead Manipulatives in Action, K–3
© 1992 Learning Resources, Inc.

Names for One-Half

 Objective

To find equivalent fractions for one-half.

Vocabulary
equivalent

Materials
Overhead Fraction Circles, transparencies of pages 106 and 118, a blank transparency, overhead pens; *Circular Fraction Sets*, student copies of pages 106 and 118, pencils, colored cutouts of fraction pieces (pages 107–108), paste

Warm-Up
Play the Fraction Flash Game. Display the transparency of page 106 on the projector. Tell children that you are going to show a fraction picture to them for only a few seconds and then shut off the projector. Ask them to respond quickly. After each fraction, ask children how they would write the fraction for each picture. Try to cover as many fractional situations as possible to show 1/2 using halves, fourths, sixths, and eighths.

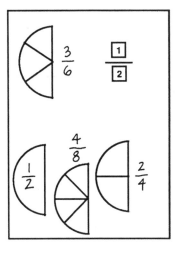

Activity
Distribute page 106 and sets of circular fractions. Display the transparency of page 106 on the projector. Direct children to place an orange piece on the circle and ask what fractional part of the circle it is [1/2]. Then ask them to find other same-color fraction pieces that would cover one-half of the circle. Discuss each possibility. [2 yellow (2/4), 3 green (3/6), 4 red (4/8)]

Practice
Distribute page 118. Tell children that they are to find *equivalent* fractions for 1/2 and that they must use the same color for each problem.

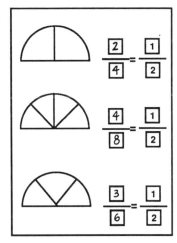

Wrap-Up
Ask volunteers to come to the projector to show equivalent fractions for 1/2. [2/4, 3/6, 4/8] Ask what they notice about the relationship of the numerator to the denominator for a fraction equivalent to 1/2. [The denominator is twice as large as the numerator.] Challenge children to predict fractions that would be equivalent to 1/2 if the circle was divided into tenths or twelfths, or even hundredths. Also ask whether it is possible to show 1/2 if the circle is divided into an odd number of parts.

Sample Solutions:

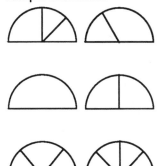

Extension Activity
Using page 106, the colored cutouts of the fraction circle pieces (pages 107 and 108), and paste, challenge children to find all possible ways to show 1/2 using same- and different-colored circular fraction pieces. This activity will enhance their intuitive knowledge necessary for understanding addition with fractional numbers.

Fraction Circles

Names for 1/2

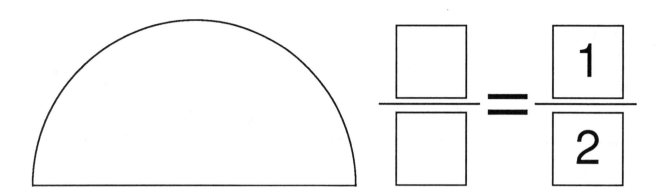

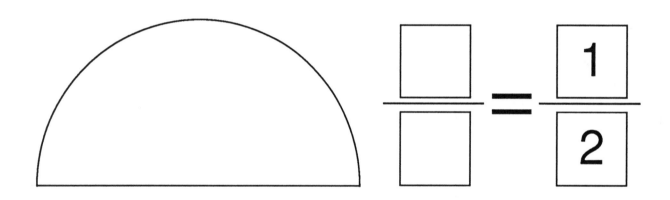

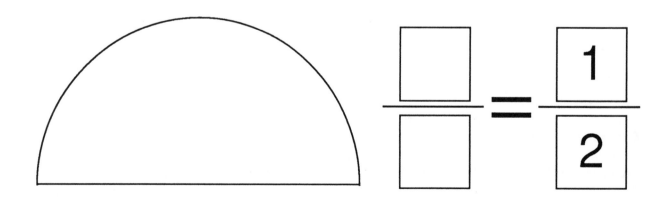

Overhead Manipulatives in Action, K–3
© 1992 Learning Resources, Inc.

Names for One

Objectives

To find equivalent fractions for one.
To find fractional parts to make one.

Vocabulary

equivalent

Materials

Overhead Fraction Circles, transparencies of pages 106 and 120, a blank
transparency, overhead pens; *Circular Fraction Sets*, student copies of page 120,
pencils, colored cutouts of fraction pieces (pages 107–108), paste

Warm-Up

Distribute page 106 and sets of circular fractions. Display the transparency of
page 106 on the projector. Direct children to find same-color fractional pieces to
cover the circle and to write a fraction for that picture. [Solutions should include
2/2, 3/3, 4/4, 6/6, and 8/8.] Ask what children notice about the relationship of the
numerator to the denominator for fractions equivalent to number 1. [The
denominator is equal to the numerator.] Challenge students to predict fractions
that would be equivalent to 1 if the circle was divided into tenths or twelfths or
even ninety-ninths!

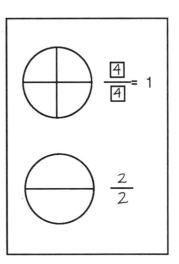

Activity

Distribute page 120 and sets of circular fractions. Ask children to find two ways
to cover the circles using different-colored fraction pieces. Ask volunteers to
come to the projector to show their solutions. This activity will enable children
to think more flexibly about quantities to make 1 as well as enhance their
intuitive knowledge necessary for understanding addition with fractional
numbers.

Practice

Working in cooperative groups of three or four, using page 120, the colored
fraction circle cutouts (pages 107–108) and paste, each child should find and
show at least two ways for making 1. Allow children to request as many copies
of page 120 as they need in order to find all the possible solutions.

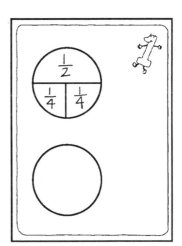

Wrap-Up

Have each group "show and tell" their solutions to the class. After the
discussion, display their solutions on the bulletin board or bind them into a book
for all to look at their leisure.

Sample Solutions:

Extension Activity

Encourage some children to think about how they would write addition
sentences such as 1/2 + 1/4 + 1/4 = 1 or 1/2 + 2/4 = 1 for each of their solutions.

Fraction Circles

Names for One

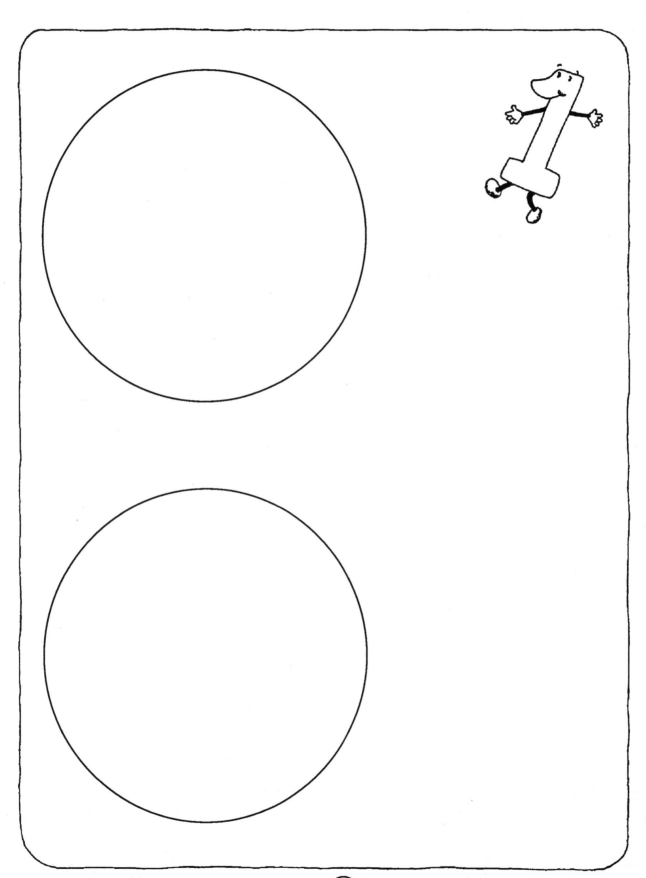

Overhead Manipulatives in Action, K–3
© 1992 Learning Resources, Inc.

Student Progress Chart

Name _____

Grade _____ Year _____

School _____

Teacher _____

Content	Comments	Content	Comments
Three Bear Family™		**Base Ten Blocks**	
Sort and Classify		Numbers for Blocks	
Patterns		Blocks for Numbers	
Count and Compare		Trade Up	
Acting out Addition		Trade Down	
Acting out Subtraction		Understanding Addition	
Making Arrangements		Understanding Subtraction	
Attribute Blocks		**Clocks**	
Attribute Shapes		Hour Time	
Two Groups		Half-Hour Time	
Patterns		Quarter-Hour Time	
One-Way Change		Minute Time	
One–Two–Three Game		Time from Now	
More Shapes		Time Ago	
Pattern Blocks		**Coins**	
Sort and Classify		Penny, Nickel, Dime	
Copies of Blocks		Quarter	
Larger Block Shapes		Half-Dollar	
Copy Cat		Counting Money	
Exploring Symmetry		Going Shopping	
Symmetry of Other Shapes		Making Change	
Numbers 1–100		**Fraction Circles**	
Sets and Numerals		One and Halves	
Count On, Count Back		Fourths and Eighths	
Count and Compare		Thirds and Sixths	
Even or Odd		Compare Fractions	
Number Patterns		Names for 1/2	
The Largest, the Smallest		Names for One	

Dear Family,

    Your child _____ *is learning*
about _____ *this week in school.*
Here is an activity that can help your child learn more about the concept.

_____
_____
_____
_____
_____
_____
_____
_____
_____
_____
_____
_____
_____
_____
_____
_____
_____
_____
_____

_____   _____
Date   Teacher

Dear _____,

_____

_____

_____

_____

_____

_____

Date _____   _____ Teacher

GOOD WORK!

▼ ▼ ▼

TO _____

FOR _____

Date _____   _____ **Teacher**

Overhead Math

▼ ▼
▼ ▼
▼ ▼

AWARD

TO
_____

FOR
_____

Date
_____

Teacher
_____